Contents

Daily Enrich

Lesson 1-1 Numbers 1
Lesson 1-2 Number Patterns • Algebra 2
Lesson 1-3 Understand Addition and Subtraction. 3
Lesson 1-4 Problem Solving Skill: Reading for Math ... 4

Lesson 2-1 Order Property and Zero Property • Algebra ... 5
Lesson 2-2 Count On to Add 6
Lesson 2-3 Addition Patterns • Algebra 7
Lesson 2-4 Add Three Numbers 8

Lesson 3-1 Count Back to Subtract 9
Lesson 3-2 Subtract All and Subtract Zero. 10
Lesson 3-3 Relate Addition to Subtraction • Algebra ... 11
Lesson 3-4 Missing Number • Algebra 12
Lesson 3-5 Names for Numbers • Algebra 13
Lesson 3-6 Problem Solving Skill: Reading for Math. .. 14

Lesson 4-1 Use Doubles to Add or Subtract 15
Lesson 4-2 Use 10 to Add and Subtract 9 16
Lesson 4-3 Use 10 to Add and Subtract 7 and 8 17
Lesson 4-4 Fact Families 18

Lesson 5-1 Tens 19
Lesson 5-2 Tens and Ones 20
Lesson 5-3 Place Value to 100 21
Lesson 5-4 Read and Write Numbers. 22
Lesson 5-5 Estimate Numbers 23
Lesson 5-6 Problem Solving Skill: Reading for Math. .. 24

Lesson 6-1 Compare Numbers • Algebra 25
Lesson 6-2 Order Numbers 26
Lesson 6-3 Skip-Counting Patterns • Algebra 27
Lesson 6-4 Ordinal Numbers 28
Lesson 6-5 Even and Odd Numbers 29

Lesson 7-1 Pennies, Nickels, and Dimes 30
Lesson 7-2 Count Coin Collections 31
Lesson 7-3 Money and Place Value 32
Lesson 7-4 Quarters and Half Dollars. 33
Lesson 7-5 Make Equal Amounts 34
Lesson 7-6 Problem Solving Skill: Reading for Math. .. 35

Lesson 8-1 Dollar 36
Lesson 8-2 Dollars and Cents 37
Lesson 8-3 Compare Money Amounts 38
Lesson 8-4 Make Change. 39

Lesson 9-1 Time to the Hour and Half Hour 40
Lesson 9-2 Time to Five Minutes 41
Lesson 9-3 Time to the Quarter Hour 42
Lesson 9-4 Time Before and After the Hour. 43
Lesson 9-5 Problem Solving Skill: Reading for Math. .. 44

Lesson 10-1 A.M. and P.M. 45
Lesson 10-2 Elapsed Time 46
Lesson 10-3 Calendar 47
Lesson 10-4 Time Relationships • Algebra 48

Lesson 11-1 Picture and Bar Graphs. 49
Lesson 11-2 Surveys 50
Lesson 11-3 Make a Bar Graph 51
Lesson 11-4 Pictographs 52
Lesson 11-5 Line Plots 53

Lesson 11-6 Different Ways to Show Data 54
Lesson 11-7 Problem Solving Skill: Reading for Math 55

Lesson 12-1 Explore Regrouping 56
Lesson 12-2 Addition with Sums to 20 57
Lesson 12-3 Addition with Greater Numbers 58
Lesson 12-4 Renaming Numbers • Algebra 59

Lesson 13-1 Mental Math: Add Tens 60
Lesson 13-2 Count on Tens and Ones to Add 61
Lesson 13-3 Decide When to Regroup 62
Lesson 13-4 Add a 1-Digit and a 2-Digit Number 63
Lesson 13-5 Add 2-Digit Numbers 64
Lesson 13-6 Practice Addition 65
Lesson 13-7 Problem Solving Skill: Reading for Math 66

Lesson 14-1 Rewrite Addition 67
Lesson 14-2 Practice 2-Digit Addition 68
Lesson 14-3 Check Addition • Algebra 69
Lesson 14-4 Estimate Sums 70
Lesson 14-5 Add Three Numbers • Algebra 71

Lesson 15-1 Mental Math: Subtract Tens 72
Lesson 15-2 Mental Math: Count Back Tens and Ones to Subtract 73
Lesson 15-3 Decide When to Regroup 74
Lesson 15-4 Subtract a 1-Digit Number from a 2-Digit Number 75
Lesson 15-5 Subtract 2-Digit Numbers 76
Lesson 15-6 Practice Subtraction 77
Lesson 15-7 Problem Solving Skill: Reading for Math 78

Lesson 16-1 Rewrite 2-Digit Subtraction 79
Lesson 16-2 Practice 2-Digit Subtraction 80
Lesson 16-3 Check Subtraction • Algebra 81
Lesson 16-4 Estimate Differences 82
Lesson 16-5 Mental Math: Strategies 83

Lesson 17-1 Nonstandard Units of Length 84
Lesson 17-2 Measure to the Nearest Inch 85
Lesson 17-3 Inch, Foot, and Yard 86
Lesson 17-4 Centimeter and Meter 87
Lesson 17-5 Problem Solving Skill: Reading for Math 88

Lesson 18-1 Explore Capacity 89
Lesson 18-2 Fluid Ounce, Cup, Pint, Quart, and Gallon • Algebra 90
Lesson 18-3 Ounce and Pound 91
Lesson 18-4 Milliliter and Liter 92
Lesson 18-5 Gram and Kilogram 93
Lesson 18-6 Temperature 94

Lesson 19-1 3-Dimensional Figures 95
Lesson 19-2 2-Dimensional Shapes 96
Lesson 19-3 2-Dimensional and 3-Dimensional Relationships 97
Lesson 19-4 Combine Shapes 98
Lesson 19-5 Describe Patterns • Algebra 99
Lesson 19-6 Problem Solving Skill: Reading for Math 100

Lesson 20-1 Congruence 101
Lesson 20-2 Symmetry 102
Lesson 20-3 Slides, Flips, and Turns 103
Lesson 20-4 Perimeter 104
Lesson 20-5 Area 105

Lesson 21-1 Hundreds 106
Lesson 21-2 Hundreds, Tens, and Ones 107
Lesson 21-3 Place Value Through Hundreds 108
Lesson 21-4 Explore Place Value to Thousands 109
Lesson 21-5 Problem Solving Skill: Reading for Math 110

Lesson 22-1 Compare Numbers • Algebra.. 111
Lesson 22-2 Order Numbers on a Number Line.. 112
Lesson 22-3 Order Numbers.. 113
Lesson 22-4 Number Patterns • Algebra.. 114
Lesson 22-5 Count Forward, Count Backward 115

Lesson 23-1 Add Hundreds... 116
Lesson 23-2 Regroup Ones... 117
Lesson 23-3 Regroup Tens 119
Lesson 23-4 Problem Solving Skill: Reading for Math 119

Lesson 24-1 Subtract Hundreds 120
Lesson 24-2 Regroup Tens as Ones 121
Lesson 24-3 Regroup Hundreds as Tens.. 122
Lesson 24-4 Estimate, Add, and Subtract Money Amounts 123

Lesson 25-1 Unit Fractions 124
Lesson 25-2 Fractions Equal to 1... 125
Lesson 25-3 Other Fractions.. 126
Lesson 25-4 Unit Fractions of a Group 127
Lesson 25-5 Other Fractions of a Group 128
Lesson 25-6 Compare Fractions • Algebra.. 129
Lesson 25-7 Problem Solving Skill: Reading for Math 130

Lesson 26-1 Explore Probability 131
Lesson 26-2 More Likely, Equally Likely, or Less Likely 132
Lesson 26-3 Make Predictions... 133

Lesson 27-1 Range and Mode 134
Lesson 27-2 Median 135
Lesson 27-3 Coordinate Graphs • Algebra 136
Lesson 27-4 Line Graphs 137
Lesson 27-5 Problem Solving Skill: Reading for Math 138

Lesson 28-1 Explore Equal Groups... 139
Lesson 28-2 Repeated Addition and Multiplication 140
Lesson 28-3 Use Arrays to Multiply • Algebra.. 141
Lesson 28-4 Repeated Subtraction and Division 142
Lesson 28-5 Divide to Find Equal Shares 143

Name _____

Numbers

Many animals at the animal shelter need homes. People come to the shelter to look for a pet.

Complete.
Look at the picture. Find the right numbers for each question.

1. How many more cats than dogs are at the shelter?

_____

_____

2. What time is it?

_____

_____

3. How many people are at the shelter?

_____

_____

4. How many more fish than turtles are at the shelter?

_____

_____

5. How many animals are there at the animal shelter?

_____

Number Patterns • Algebra

Count by twos. Draw a ◯ on each number.

Count by threes. Draw a ✕ on each number.

Count by fours. Draw a ▢ on each number.

Count by fives. Draw a △ on each number.

1	2	3	4	5	6	7	8	9	10
11	12	13	14	15	16	17	18	19	20
21	22	23	24	25	26	27	28	29	30
31	32	33	34	35	36	37	38	39	40
41	42	43	44	45	46	47	48	49	50
51	52	53	54	55	56	57	58	59	60
61	62	63	64	65	66	67	68	69	70
71	72	73	74	75	76	77	78	79	80
81	82	83	84	85	86	87	88	89	90
91	92	93	94	95	96	97	98	99	100

Use with Grade 2, Chapter 1, Lesson 2, pages 5–6.

Name _____

Understand Addition and Subtraction

Murray Frog, Freddy Frog, and Franny Frog jump on rocks across the pond.

Write an addition or subtraction sentence that tells about the jumps.

1. Murray Frog jumps back 1.

He starts on 9.

Where does he land?

_____

Murray Frog lands on _____.

Franny Frog jumps back 3.

She starts on 9.

Where does she land?

_____

Franny Frog lands on _____.

2. Freddy Frog jumps ahead 2.

He starts on 8.

Where does he land?

_____

Freddy Frog lands on _____.

Franny Frog jumps ahead 3.

She starts on 4.

Where does she land?

_____

Franny Frog lands on _____.

3. Murray Frog jumps ahead 2.

He lands on 5.

Where did he start?

_____

Murray Frog starts on _____.

Freddy Frog jumps back 3.

He lands on 7.

Where did he start?

_____

Freddy Frog starts on _____.

Problem Solving Skill: Reading for Math

Maria and Ellie are friends. They collect dolls from around the world. They keep the dolls on 2 shelves. Maria has 10 dolls in her collection. Ellie has 8 dolls in her collection.

Choose the best answer. Fill in the ◯.

1. Maria gave her sister 2 dolls. How many dolls are left in Maria's collection?

Ⓐ 6

Ⓑ 4

Ⓒ 8

Ⓓ 2

2. Ellie received 3 more dolls as presents. How many dolls does Ellie have in her collection?

Ⓕ 11

Ⓖ 9

Ⓗ 12

Ⓐ 8

Solve.

3. Now how many more dolls does Ellie have than Maria? Write a number sentence.

_____

Order Property and Zero Property • Algebra

Find each sum.

Match the letter to the related fact below.

To find the secret message, write the correct letters in the boxes.

1. $\begin{array}{r}4\\+2\\\hline\end{array}$ **I**	2. $\begin{array}{r}0\\+2\\\hline\end{array}$ **T**	3. $\begin{array}{r}1\\+5\\\hline\end{array}$ **Y**
4. $\begin{array}{r}2\\+6\\\hline\end{array}$ **U**	5. $\begin{array}{r}1\\+3\\\hline\end{array}$ **G**	6. $\begin{array}{r}7\\+2\\\hline\end{array}$ **S**
7. $\begin{array}{r}3\\+7\\\hline\end{array}$ **O**	8. $\begin{array}{r}4\\+3\\\hline\end{array}$ **R**	9. $\begin{array}{r}5\\+6\\\hline\end{array}$ **H**

☐ $\begin{array}{r}5\\+1\\\hline\end{array}$ ☐ $\begin{array}{r}7\\+3\\\hline\end{array}$ ☐ $\begin{array}{r}6\\+2\\\hline\end{array}$ | ☐ $\begin{array}{r}3\\+1\\\hline\end{array}$ ☐ $\begin{array}{r}7\\+3\\\hline\end{array}$ ☐ $\begin{array}{r}2\\+0\\\hline\end{array}$

☐ $\begin{array}{r}2\\+0\\\hline\end{array}$ ☐ $\begin{array}{r}6\\+5\\\hline\end{array}$ ☐ $\begin{array}{r}2\\+4\\\hline\end{array}$ ☐ $\begin{array}{r}2\\+7\\\hline\end{array}$

☐ $\begin{array}{r}3\\+4\\\hline\end{array}$ ☐ $\begin{array}{r}2\\+4\\\hline\end{array}$ ☐ $\begin{array}{r}3\\+1\\\hline\end{array}$ ☐ $\begin{array}{r}6\\+5\\\hline\end{array}$ ☐ $\begin{array}{r}2\\+0\\\hline\end{array}$

Count On to Add

Write an addition sentence for each question about a number line.

1. Alex started at 14.

He counted on 3.

Where did he land?

_____

2. Karen started at 15.

She counted on 3.

Where did she land?

_____

3. Maria started at 16.

She counted on 2.

Where did she land?

_____

4. Ricky started at 12.

He counted on 3.

Where did he land?

_____

5. Ann started at 17.

She counted on 3.

Where did she land?

_____

6. John started at 18.

He counted on 1.

Where did he land?

_____

7. Brian started at 17.

He counted on 2.

Where did he land?

_____

8. Cara started at 19.

She counted on 2.

Where did she land?

_____

Use with Grade 2, Chapter 2, Lesson 2, pages 19–20.

Addition Patterns • Algebra

Look at the rule.
Complete the table.

1. Rule: Add 3.

Input	Output
	9
	10
	11
	12

2. Rule: Add 7.

Input	Output
	10
	11
	12
	13

3. Rule: Add 4.

Input	Output
	4
	5
	6
	7

4. Rule: Add 5.

Input	Output
	11
	12
	13
	14

5. Rule: Add 9.

Input	Output
	10
	11
	12
	13

6. Rule: Add 10.

Input	Output
	14
	16
	18
	20

Add Three Numbers • Algebra

This is a map of the playground at Pete's school.
The map shows the number of units between each playground toy.

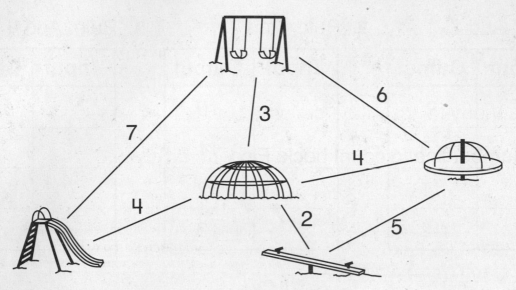

Find the total number of units for the path.
Write a number sentence to show how you found the total.

1.  to  to to

_____ units + _____ units + _____ units = _____ units

2.  to to  to

_____ units + _____ units + _____ units = _____ units

3. Pete started on the seesaw.
He went on the monkey bars.
Next he had fun on the slide.
Then he played on the swing.
How many units did Pete travel?

_____ + _____ + _____ = _____

Name _____

Count Back to Subtract

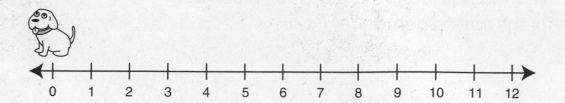

Juan sells many things at the pet store.

Use the number line to count back. Find the difference.

1. There are 10 cat toys. Mai buys 2 toys for her cat. Ali buys 3 toys for his cat. How many cat toys are left?

_____

2. The store has 12 bags of dog food. Harry buys 3 bags of dog food. Ruby buys 1 bag of dog food. How many bags of dog food are left?

_____

3. Juan sells 8 bags of dog bones. He sells 2 bags of cat treats. How many more bags of dog bones did he sell than cat treats? Explain.

_____

_____

_____

4. There are 3 bird cages and 12 cat beds. How many more cat beds than bird cages are there? Explain.

_____

_____

_____

Subtract All and Subtract Zero

Underline the number sentence that is correct.
Then fix the wrong sentence.

1. $14 - 0 = 0$ $14 - \cancel{0} = 0$ (14 above)

$14 - 0 = 14$ _____

2. $5 - 5 = 0$ _____

$5 - 0 = 0$ _____

3. $3 - 3 = 3$ _____

$3 - 0 = 3$ _____

4. $8 - 0 = 0$ _____

$8 - 8 = 0$ _____

Read the sentences. Write the difference.

5. 6 seals are in the pool. 3 seals leave the pool. 3 more seals leave, too. How many seals are left in the pool?

_____

_____

6. 10 bears are in a cave. All the bears stay. How many bears are left in the cave?

_____

_____

Use with Grade 2, Chapter 3, Lesson 2, pages 35–36.

Name _____

Relate Addition to Subtraction

	Stamps in Our Collections
Pete	[8 stamps]
Polly	[6 stamps]
Paco	[6 stamps]
Paula	[9 stamps]

Each stands for 1 stamp.

Pete has _____ stamps. Polly has _____ stamps.

Paco has _____ stamps. Paula has _____ stamps.

Write an addition sentence.
Write a related subtraction sentence.

	Addition Sentence	Subtraction Sentence
1. Pete and Paco		
2. Pete and Paula		
3. Polly and Paco		
4. Paco and Paula		
5. Polly and Paula		

Missing Number • Algebra

Write a number sentence.
Find the mystery number.

1. Add 8 to me to get 13.

Who am I?

☐ + ☐ = ☐

The mystery number is

_____.

2. Add 7 to me to get 16.

Who am I?

☐ + ☐ = ☐

The mystery number is

_____.

3. Subtract me from 11 to get 5.

Who am I?

☐ − ☐ = ☐

The mystery number is

_____.

4. Subtract me from 14 to get 6.

Who am I?

☐ − ☐ = ☐

The mystery number is

_____.

5. Add 9 to me to get 12.

Who am I?

☐ + ☐ = ☐

The mystery number is

_____.

6. Subtract me from 15 to get 8.

Who am I?

☐ − ☐ = ☐

The mystery number is

_____.

Use with Grade 2, Chapter 3, Lesson 4, pages 41–42.

Names for Numbers • Algebra

Rory and Margaret are playing cards. They use the numbers on the cards. Numbers can be used more than once.

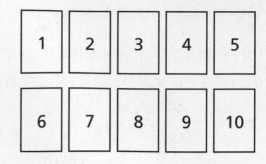

1. Use addition to find ways to make the number 7.

_____

2. Use subtraction to find the ways to make the number 8.

_____

3. Use addition and subtraction to find ways to make the number 6.

_____

Circle your answer.

4. Which number sentence is not equal to 5?

$10 - 5$

$3 + 2$

$6 - 2$

$4 + 1$

5. Which number sentence is not equal to 10?

$1 + 4 + 6$

$3 + 4 + 3$

$5 + 3 + 2$

$6 + 1 + 3$

Problem Solving Skill: Reading for Math
Compare and Contrast

One school gives instrument lessons. 18 children take piano lessons.
6 children take violin lessons. 2 children take drum lessons.

Choose the best answer. Fill in the ◯ .

1. How many more children
take piano lessons than
violin lessons?

Ⓐ 12

Ⓑ 8

Ⓒ 6

Ⓓ 4

2. How many more children
take piano lessons than
drum lessons?

Ⓕ 13

Ⓖ 14

Ⓗ 15

Ⓐ 16

Solve.

3. Write number sentences to compare the piano group with the
violin group and drum group combined. Explain.

_____

_____

4. Four children stopped taking piano lessons. How does the piano
group compare with the violin group? Explain.

_____

_____

Use Doubles to Add and Subtract

1. Sara has 3¢ on Friday.
Each day she doubles her money.
Write the amount Sara has each day.

Friday	Saturday	Sunday
+3¢	___ + ___ = ___	___ + ___ = ___

How much does Sara have on Monday? _____

Subtract.
Write the doubles fact that gives the same difference.

2.
$$\begin{array}{r} 14 \\ -\ 8 \\ \hline 6 \end{array}$$

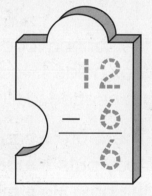

$$\begin{array}{r} 12 \\ -\ 6 \\ \hline 6 \end{array}$$

$$\begin{array}{r} 12 \\ -\ 9 \\ \hline \end{array}$$

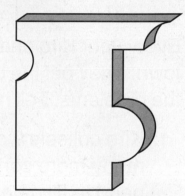

3.
$$\begin{array}{r} 16 \\ -\ 7 \\ \hline \end{array}$$

$$\begin{array}{r} 17 \\ -\ 9 \\ \hline \end{array}$$

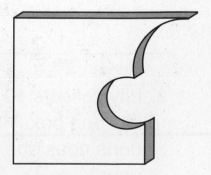

Use 10 to Add and Subtract 9

Every year Kira and her friends help with the canned food drive in town. They put the cans into boxes. Each box holds 15 cans. Complete the problems. Tell how many more cans are needed to fill each box.

1. Kira collects 9 cans. How many more cans does she need to fill a box?

_____

2. There are 6 cans in a box. Joey puts 4 more cans into the box. How many more does Joey need to fill the box?

_____

3. Lily collects 19 cans. She fills one box. How many cans does she have left over?

_____

4. Earl collects 24 cans. He fills one box. How many cans does he have left over?

_____

Use 10 to Add and Subtract 7 and 8

E 4-3
ENRICH

Play a game with a partner. Take turns.

How to Play
- Cut out the cards.
- Turn the cards over. Put them in 4 rows.
- Choose two cards.
- Keep the cards if the sums and/or differences match.
  Turn the cards over if they do not match.

The player with more cards wins.

9 + 2	10 − 7	7 + 8	10 + 2
10 + 8	10 − 8	9 − 7	8 + 8
9 + 8	5 + 7	10 + 6	10 + 7
10 + 5	9 − 6	10 + 1	9 + 9

Fact Families

Favorite Zoo Animal	Our Class	Mr. Ray's Class
lion	7	4
elephant	9	7
zebra	5	8

Use the numbers to write a fact family.

1. How many children liked the elephant best?

Our class: _____

Mr. Ray's class: _____

Total: _____

_____ + _____ = _____

_____ + _____ = _____

_____ − _____ = _____

_____ − _____ = _____

2. How many children liked the lion best?

Our class: _____

Mr. Ray's class: _____

Total: _____

_____ + _____ = _____

_____ + _____ = _____

_____ − _____ = _____

_____ − _____ = _____

3. How many children liked the zebra best?

Our class: _____

Mr. Ray's class: _____

Total: _____

_____ + _____ = _____

_____ + _____ = _____

_____ − _____ = _____

_____ − _____ = _____

Use with Grade 2, Chapter 4, Lesson 4, pages 59–60.

Name _____

Tens

Go with Ann and Mike through the music fair.
Follow groups of tens in order through 90.
Draw the path.

Tens and Ones

Tens and ones have been written in many different ways.

A long time ago, the Egyptians wrote tens and ones with these marks.

A | means 1. A ∩ means 10.

∩∩|||| is 24.

Write the number.

1. ∩∩∩∩||

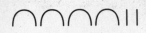

2. ∩∩∩∩
∩∩∩

_____

3. ∩∩∩∩∩∩|||||

_____

4. ∩∩∩∩∩
∩∩∩|

_____

Draw these numbers using Egyptian numerals.

5. 17

6. 50

7. 35

8. 78

Use with Grade 2, Chapter 5, Lesson 2, pages 79–80.

Place Value to 100

Help Shira find the secret numbers to open a lock.

Find the value of the underlined digits in the problems.
Circle the box that shows the value of the digit.

A ☆ means 1.

A ◯ means 10.

1. 3<u>2</u>

2. 4<u>1</u>

3. 2<u>7</u>

 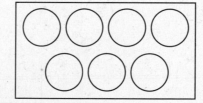

4. <u>5</u>2

 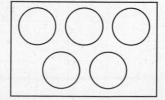

5. Write the value of each of the underlined digits.

_____ _____ _____ _____

Now Shira can open the lock.

Read and Write Numbers

Spanish word names for numbers are in the box.
Write each difference or sum.
Write the Spanish number word in the puzzle.

Spanish Number Words				
1 uno	2 dos	3 tres	4 cuatro	5 cinco
6 seis	7 siete	8 ocho	9 nueve	10 diez

1. diez − uno = __9__   2. uno + uno = _____

3. dos − uno = _____   4. dos + dos + uno = _____

5. seis + uno = _____   6. dos + uno = _____

7. cinco + cinco = _____   8. cuatro + cuatro = _____

9. dos + dos = _____

10. tres + tres = _____

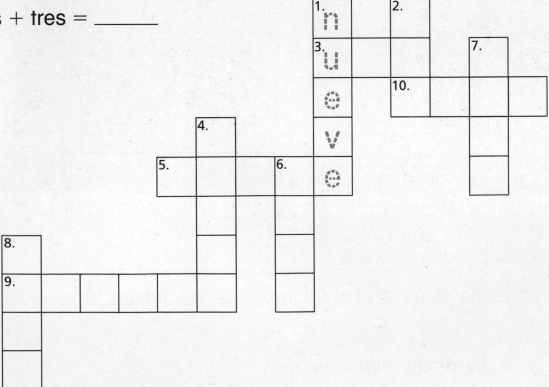

Use with Grade 2, Chapter 5, Lesson 4, pages 83–84.

Name _____

Estimate Numbers

1. Find a book.

About how many pages are in the book?

about _____ pages

2. Find a box of crayons.

About how many crayons are in the box?

about _____ crayons

3. Find a bookshelf.

About how many books are on the bookshelf?

about _____ books

4. Find a puzzle.

About how many pieces are in the puzzle?

about _____ pieces

5. Find a box of paper clips.

About how many paper clips are in the box?

about _____ paper clips

6. Find a bag of cookies.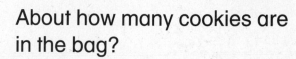

About how many cookies are in the bag?

about _____ cookies

7. Tell a friend how you estimate numbers. Write your answer here.

_____

_____

_____

Problem Solving Skill: Reading for Math
Make Predictions

 5-6 ENRICH

Two second-grade classes are planning a nature trip.
Children can vote to go to the mountains, to the beach, or to the woods.
Mr. Toy's class has 20 children. Ms. Van's class has 20 children.

 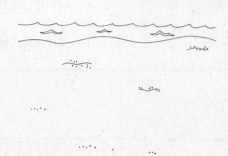 

Choose the best answer. Fill in the ◯.

1. There are 36 seats in a bus. How many buses will the second-grade classes need for the trip?

    Ⓐ 1
    Ⓑ 2
    Ⓒ 3
    Ⓓ 4

2. Ms. Van has five new children. How many children are in her class now?

    Ⓕ 25
    Ⓖ 30
    Ⓗ 35
    Ⓐ 40

Solve.

3. 5 children in each class voted for a trip to the woods. What can you predict? Will the nature trip be to the woods? Explain.

_____

4. More than half the children in each class voted to go to the beach. What can you predict about the nature trip?

_____

Use with Grade 2, Chapter 5, Lesson 6, pages 87–88.

Compare Numbers

Play a game with a partner.

Use a
and the spinners below.

Cut out the spinners.

How to Play

• Spin two 2-digit numbers.

• Write the numbers in the boxes.

• Write >, <, or = in the circle.

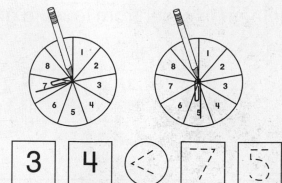

3 4 < 7 5

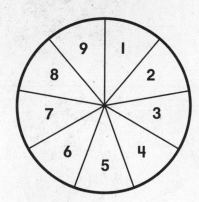
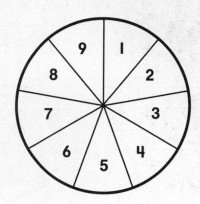

1.

2.

3.

4.

Order Numbers

The numbers are not in order.
Put them in order from least to greatest.

1.

2.

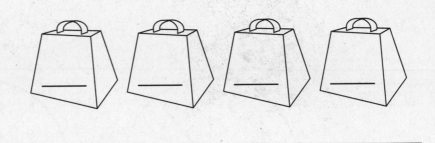

3.

4.

5.

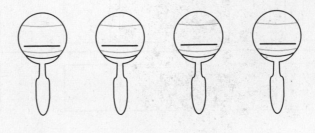

Use with Grade 2, Chapter 6, Lesson 2, pages 97–98.

Skip-Counting Patterns

Mark the train track to show where the train stops at different times during the day.

Count by twos. Draw a ☐ around each number.

Count by fours. Draw a ◯ around each number.

Count by sixes. Draw a ● on each number.

1. On which numbers does the train make 3 stops?

_____

2. On which numbers does the train only make 2 stops?

_____

Ordinal Numbers

1. Mary is second in line. Drew is right after Mary. Roger is two places behind Drew.

In what place in line is Drew? Color Drew red.

_____

In what place in line is Roger? Color Roger blue.

_____

2. Jacob is ninth in line. Gail is right after Jacob. Sue is two places ahead of Gail.

In what place in line is Gail? Color Gail yellow.

_____

In what place in line is Sue? Color Sue green.

_____

3. Barry is fourth in line. There are only two children between Barry and Lee. Lee is after Barry.

In what place in line is Lee? Color Lee purple.

_____

4. Brittany is first in line. Deon is five places behind Brittany.

In what place in line is Deon? Color Deon orange.

_____

Use with Grade 2, Chapter 6, Lesson 4, pages 103–104.

Even and Odd Numbers

Play a matching game.
Five children march in a band.
Each child wears a number.
Fill in the chart.

Sam   Mary   Paco   Elena   Chin

Clues	Name	Number
1. The tens digit is an odd number. The ones digit comes just after 7.	_____	_____
2. The ones digit is two more than the tens digit. Both digits are even numbers.	_____	_____
3. The tens digit is 2 less than the ones digit. Both digits are odd numbers.	_____	_____
4. The ones digit is 6 less than the tens digit. Both digits are odd numbers.	_____	_____
5. The tens digit is an even number. The ones digit comes just before 1.	_____	_____

Pennies, Nickels, and Dimes

Write the number of coins. Use   .

1. Ben has 4 coins. He has 26¢. One coin is a nickel. How many dimes and pennies does he have?

_____

_____

2. Jeffrey has 5 coins. He has 18¢. One coin is a dime. How many nickels and pennies does he have?

_____

_____

3. Mary has 10 coins. She has 43¢. One coin is a dime. How many nickels and pennies does she have?

_____

_____

4. Sally has 6 coins. She has 37¢. One coin is a nickel. How many dimes and pennies does she have?

_____

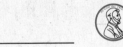
_____

5. Ben has 10 coins. He has 63¢. How many of each coin does he have?

_____

_____

_____

6. Sharla has 12 coins. She has 70¢. How many of each coin does she have?

_____

_____

_____

Use with Grade 2, Chapter 7, Lesson 1, pages 115–116.

Name _____

Count Coin Collections

Count the money in each purse.

What coin is hidden?

Write penny, nickel, dime, or quarter.

1.

Amount: 58¢

The hidden coin is a _____.

2.

Amount: 84¢

The hidden coin is a _____.

Two coins are hidden in each purse.

What two coins are they?

3.

Amount: 92¢

The hidden coins are a _____ and a _____.

4.

Amount: 75¢

The hidden coins are a _____ and a _____.

Name _____

Money and Place Value

Find out how many tens and ones there are in a money amount.

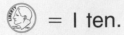 = 1 ten.   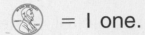 = 1 one.

1. Jen saved 26¢. Bud saved 13¢. How much did they save together? Write the amount in tens and ones.

_____ tens

_____ ones

2. Cay spent 51¢. Kim spent 22¢. How much did they spend together? Write the amount in tens and ones.

_____ tens

_____ ones

3. Nan gave Tai 79¢. Tai gave Bo 14¢. How much did Tai have left? Write the amount in tens and ones.

_____ tens

_____ ones

4. Ava earned 25¢ on Monday. She earned 55¢ on Friday. How much did she earn for both days? Write the amount in tens and ones.

_____ tens

_____ ones

5. Greg saved 95¢. He spent 33¢ for a toy. How much did he have left? Write the amount in tens and ones.

_____ tens

_____ ones

6. Alvin gave Wendy 87¢. Wendy bought a book for 55¢. How much did Wendy have left? Write the amount in tens and ones.

_____ tens

_____ ones

Use with Grade 2, Chapter 7, Lesson 3, pages 119–120.

Quarters and Half Dollars

Which coins do you need?

Use   . Draw the coins.

1. Make 50¢ using 2 coins.

2. Make 75¢ using 2 coins.

3. Make 62¢ using 4 coins.

4. Make 85¢ using 3 coins.

5. Make 55¢ using 3 coins.

6. Make 77¢ using 9 coins.

Name _____

Make Equal Amounts

Use the coins to draw the amount.

1. Cal has 3 coins that equal 27¢. Stacy has 5 coins that equal 27¢.
   Draw the coins for each person.

   Cal

   Stacy

_____

2. Jay has 7 coins that equal 44¢. Kate has 9 coins that equal 44¢.
   Draw the coins for each person.

   Jay

   Kate

_____

3. Noel has 5 coins that equal 62¢. Shea has 7 coins that equal
   62¢. Draw the coins for each person.

   Noel

   Shea

_____

Circle the group of coins with equal amounts.

4.

Use with Grade 2, Chapter 7, Lesson 5, pages 123–124.

Problem Solving Skill: Reading for Math
Cause and Effect

Joey is at the ballgame with Mom. He had been wanting to go for a long time. Joey is wearing his team shirt and cap. He says, "I can't wait for the game to start!"

Solve.

1. Joey buys a program for 30¢ and a toy bat for 49¢.

Joey spends ___79___¢ in all.

2. Joey buys a poster with 4 quarters. How much did the poster cost?

_____

3. Mom gives Joey 2 dimes and 1 quarter. Does Joey have enough money to buy a balloon for 40¢?

_____

4. A baseball card costs 35¢. Joey pays for it with 2 coins. What coins does he use?

_____

5. How do you know that Joey was excited about going to the game?

_____

_____

Dollar

Marcy saves money for one week. She needs $1.00
to buy a gift for a friend.

1. On Monday Marcy had these coins. How much more does she
need to make $1.00?

_____

2. On Friday Marcy added these coins. How much does she have
now?

_____

Complete. Draw the coins.

3. Gil has 5 coins that make $1.00.

4. Carrie has 6 coins that make $1.00.

Dollars and Cents

$2.15 $2.45 $2.95 $1.85

You have the bills and coins that are shown below.
You get more money.

Find the total amount. Write what you can buy.

1.

You get 25¢ more.

Now you have $ _2.15_ .

What can you buy?

a toy car or boat

2.

You get 2 nickels more.

Now you have $ _____ .

What can you buy?

_____

3.

You get 1 quarter more.

Now you have $ _____ .

What can you buy?

_____

Compare Money Amounts

Play with a partner. Take turns.
You will need a button and play money.

How to Play

• Drop the button on the gameboard.

• Show the amount with play money.

• Compare money amounts.

The player with more money gets a point.
The first player with 10 points wins.

1 dollar 1 quarter 2 dimes $1.45	1 dollar 2 quarters 5 pennies	2 dollars 4 dimes 1 nickel
2 dollars 5 nickels 10 pennies	1 dollar 1 half dollar 3 quarters	2 dollars 4 quarters 3 dimes
2 dollars 2 half dollars 5 nickels	1 dollar 3 dimes 6 nickels	2 dollars 5 dimes 8 nickels

38

Use with Grade 2, Chapter 8, Lesson 3, pages 137–138.

Name _____

Make Change

POP CORN 38¢

45¢

WATER 52¢

27¢

60¢

32¢

---

1. Greta has these coins. She buys a bottle of water. What is her change?

Coins: __55__ ¢

Change: __3__ ¢

---

2. Megan has these coins. She buys a bag of popcorn. What is her change?

Coins: _____ ¢

Change: _____ ¢

---

3. Ben has this coin. He buys a hot dog. What is his change?

Coins: _____ ¢

Change: _____ ¢

---

4. You have these coins. What will you buy? What will be your change?

Coins: _____ ¢

Buy: _____

Change: _____ ¢

Time to the Hour and Half Hour

What time will most likely be next in the pattern?
Draw the clock hands on the clock. Write the time.

1.

11:00

2.

_____

3.

_____

4.

_____

Use with Grade 2, Chapter 9, Lesson 1, pages 155–156.

Time to Five Minutes

Each clock shows when the bus leaves the bus station.

Use the pictures to solve the problems.

1. Ben takes Bus A to West Point. The bus takes 25 minutes. At what time does Ben get to West Point?

Start time — 10:00

End time — 10:25

2. Jessie takes Bus B to Pearl River. The bus takes 35 minutes. At what time does Jessie get to Pearl River?

Start time — __:__

End time — __:__

3. Sally takes Bus C to Center City. The bus takes 45 minutes. At what time does Sally get to Center City?

Start time — __:__

End time — __:__

4. Suki takes Bus D to Allentown. The bus takes 20 minutes. At what time does Suki get to Allentown?

Start time — __:__

End time — __:__

Time to the Quarter Hour

Play a game with a partner. You will need 14 ◯.

clock	clock	12:00	clock
6:15	**How to Play** Cover each box with a counter. Take turns.		clock
clock	• Remove two counters.		clock
clock	• Keep them if the two times match. Return them if they do not. The winner is the player with the most counters.		clock
3:45	clock	clock	11:45

The time is 8:45. What time will it be in 15 minutes?

_____

Use with Grade 2, Chapter 9, Lesson 3, pages 159–160.

Time Before and After the Hour

Draw the clock hands to show the end time
of each activity.

Start time	Activity	End time
	Brush your teeth.	
	Eat lunch.	
	Do your homework.	
	Make the bed.	
	Wash the dog.	

Problem Solving Skill: Reading for Math
Sequence of Events

Read the story.

At 4:15, I am going to the fair.

My dad and I can't wait to get there.

At 5 o'clock, we'll get something to eat.

Corn dogs are always such a treat!

At 20 minutes after 6, we'll look at the animals:

Cows, sheep, goats, and even some camels.

Before we go home at 9:05,

We'll take a bumper-car ride at 8:45.

Choose the best answer. Fill in the ○.

1. At what time will the boy go to the fair?

Ⓐ quarter to 4

Ⓑ 15 minutes before 4

Ⓒ quarter to 5

Ⓓ quarter after 4

2. What will the boy do first?

Ⓕ Get something to eat.

Ⓖ Drive a bumper car.

Ⓗ Look at animals.

Ⓐ Go home.

Solve.

3. When will the boy ride the bumper cars? Write the time in two ways. _____

_____

4. When will the boy look at the animals? Write the time in two ways. _____

ways. _____

Use with Grade 2, Chapter 9, Lesson 5, pages 163–164.

A.M. and P.M.

Matt is going on a class trip tomorrow. Everyone is excited. The bus will pick up Matt's class at 9:30 A.M. First the class will go to a park. Then they will visit a science museum that has a playground of the planets.

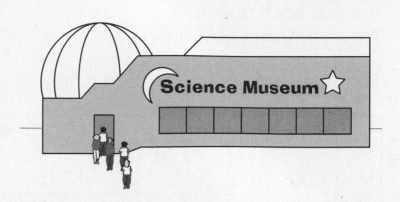

Circle the better time.

1. Matt has to wake up at _____ for his trip.

   7:00 A.M.   7:00 P.M.

2. The bus ride to the city will take 2 hours. The class will arrive at _____.

   11:30 A.M.   11:30 P.M.

3. The class will enjoy lunch in the park at _____.

   12:00 A.M.   12:00 P.M.

4. If they take an hour for lunch, the class will leave for the science museum at _____.

   1:00 A.M.   1:00 P.M.

5. After spending 3 hours at the museum, the class will get on the bus at _____.

   4:00 A.M.   4:00 P.M.

6. The bus trip home will take 2 hours. The bus will arrive at _____.

   6:00 A.M.   6:00 P.M.

Elapsed Time

Answer each question.
Then complete the schedule.

The Brown family goes to see a play.

Leave home	Arrive in city	Lunch begins	Lunch ends	Play starts
11:00	12:00	12:15	_____:_____	2:00
Play ends	Pick up car	Leave the city	Arrive home	Eat dinner
_____:_____	4:15	_____:_____	5:30	_____:_____

1. The Browns arrive 15 minutes before lunch begins.
   At what time do the Browns arrive? _____:_____

2. Lunch ends 45 minutes before the play starts.
   At what time does lunch end? _____:_____

3. The play lasts 2 hours. At what time does
   the play end? _____:_____

4. The Browns leave for home 15 minutes after
   they pick up the car. At what time do they leave
   the city? _____:_____

5. It takes the Browns one-half hour to make
   dinner after they get home. At what time do
   they eat? _____:_____

Use with Grade 2, Chapter 10, Lesson 2, pages 173–174.

Name_____

Calendar

November has 30 days. It starts on Sunday.
Fill in the calendar.

Sunday	Monday	Tuesday	Wednesday	Thursday	Friday	Saturday

Use the calendar to answer the questions.

1. How many Fridays are there in November?
Draw tally marks to show how many.
_____

2. How many Mondays are there in November?
Draw tally marks to show how many.
_____

3. Are there more Mondays or Fridays in
November?   _____

4. October is the month before November.
On what day of the week does October end? _____

5. December is the month after November.
On what day of the week does December start?_____

6. Thanksgiving day is November 26.
School is closed Thanksgiving and the day
after. For how many days is school open in
November ?   _____

Time Relationships • Algebra

Sometimes it is a good idea to plan ahead.

Read the plans. Then find the correct time. Use the chart.

Time Relationships
1 minute = 60 seconds
1 hour = 60 minutes
1 day = 24 hours
1 week = 7 days
1 year = 12 months

1. It is October. Shana's birthday is 2 months away. What month is Shana's birthday?

_____

2. Carey is going to play the violin in a recital. Today is August 2. She has 1 more week to practice. What day will the recital be?

_____

3. The Wu family is planning a trip. They will be camping for the first 3 days. Then they will visit friends for 4 days. How long is their trip?

_____

4. Lola can tie her shoes in about 30 seconds. It takes Mel about 30 seconds more to tie his shoes. About how long does it take Mel to tie his shoes?

_____

5. Hal is moving. His parents plan to leave their old home at 9:00 A.M. After driving for 10 hours, they will stop in a hotel for the night. They plan to be at their new home by 9:00 A.M. the next morning. How long will their trip take?

_____

6. Sara wrote a book. It took her 8 months to write the first half. After another 4 months she finished the book. How long did it take Sara to write the book?

_____

Use with Grade 2, Chapter 10, Lesson 4, pages 179–180.

Picture and Bar Graphs

Lulu is planning a party. She needs to buy
ice cream. She asks her friends to name their
favorite flavor.

Cherry is the favorite of 3 friends.
Vanilla is the favorite of 6 friends.
Strawberry is the favorite of 5 friends.
Chocolate is the favorite of 7 friends.

1. Make a picture graph of the information.

 stands for 1 friend.

Favorite Flavor of Ice Cream	
Vanilla	
Chocolate	
Strawberry	
Cherry	

2. Use the picture graph to make a bar graph.

```
8
7
6
5
4
3
2
1
0
   Vanilla  Chocolate  Strawberry  Cherry
```

Name _____

Surveys

Ask your classmates to vote on their favorite color.
Make a tally mark for each vote. Each classmate gets
one vote.

Red	Blue	Yellow	Green	Orange	Purple

Use the chart to make a pictograph.
Draw one ♥ for each vote.

Our Favorite Colors

Red	
Blue	
Yellow	
Green	
Orange	
Purple	

Each ♥ stands for one classmate.

Use your graph to answer each question.

1. Which color got the most votes? _____

2. Which color got the fewest votes? _____

3. How many children liked green the best? _____

4. Write a question about the graph. Then answer it. _____

_____

Use with Grade 2, Chapter 11, Lesson 2, pages 191–192.

Make a Bar Graph

Solve each problem to find out how many votes each pet got. Then make a bar graph. Write a title for the graph.

1. Dogs got 8 votes in all. Cats got 3 more votes than dogs.

Cats got _____ votes.

2. Birds got 4 fewer votes than cats.

Birds got _____ votes.

3. Turtles got 3 fewer votes than birds.

Turtles got _____ votes.

4. Fish got 2 more votes than turtles.

Fish got _____ votes.

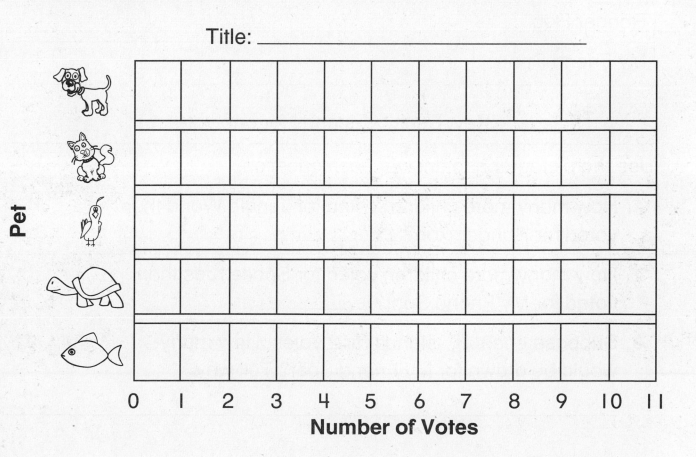

Title: _____

Pet

Number of Votes

0 1 2 3 4 5 6 7 8 9 10 11

Name _____

Pictographs

Mr. Johnson's students voted for their favorite TV shows.

Each child had one vote.

Jungle World	Space Kids	Ranger Rob	My Friend Spot
9	11	5	8

Use the information above to make a pictograph.

My Favorite TV Show

Jungle World	
Space Kids	
Ranger Rob	
My Friend Spot	

Key: Each 🧍 stands for one vote.

Use the pictograph to answer each question.

1. How many more children voted for Jungle World than voted for Ranger Rob? _____

2. How many more children voted for Space Kids than voted for My Friend Spot? _____

3. Suppose each 🧍 stands for 2 votes. How many 🧍 would be drawn for My Friend Spot? Tell why.

_____

Use with Grade 2, Chapter 11, Lesson 4, pages 195–196.

Line Plots

Areta's class wants to start a book club.
Children will trade books.
They will talk about what they read.

Areta owns 6 books.
Find out how many books her classmates own.

1. 4 children own 2 more books than Areta.
How many books does each of them own? _____

2. 3 children own 5 fewer books than Areta.
How many books does each of them own? _____

3. 2 children own 2 fewer books than Areta.
How many books does each of them own? _____

4. 3 children own the same number of books as Areta.
How many books does each of them own? _____

Fill in the line plot to show the number of books
each child owns. Include Areta.

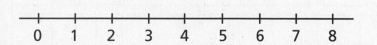

0 1 2 3 4 5 6 7 8

Name _____

Different Ways to Show Data

Find out how many players are on each
kind of team.

Record the data in the tally chart.

Show the data in a pictograph and a bar graph.

Sport	Baseball	Basketball	Football	Soccer
Tally	IIII IIII	IIII	IIII IIII I	IIII IIII I
Total	9			

Sports Teams	
Baseball	
Basketball	
Football	
Soccer	

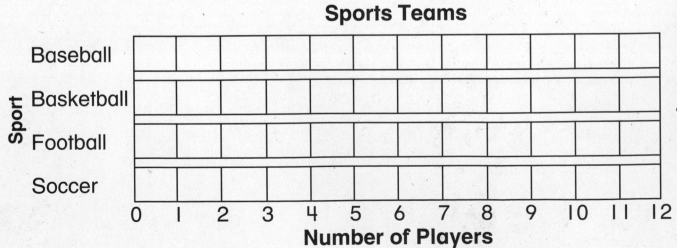

Key: Each 🏃 stands for 2 players.

Sports Teams

Sport: Baseball, Basketball, Football, Soccer

Number of Players: 0 1 2 3 4 5 6 7 8 9 10 11 12

Use with Grade 2, Chapter 11, Lesson 6, pages 199–200.

Problem Solving Skill: Reading for Math

Make Inferences

Ms. Yee has a beautiful garden. This year Ms. Yee grew 14 tomatoes, 8 peppers, and 8 heads of lettuce. There were also 6 cucumbers and 7 beets. Next year Ms. Yee hopes to have a bigger garden.

Solve.

1. What kind of dish do you think Ms. Yee will fix? Tell why.

_____

2. Why do you think Ms. Yee grows her own fruits and vegetables?

_____

3. Will Ms. Yee be able to grow more fruits and vegetables next year? Explain.

_____

_____

Choose the best answer. Fill in the ◯.

4. How many more tomatoes were there than cucumbers?

   Ⓐ 9   Ⓒ 6

   Ⓑ 7   Ⓓ 8

5. How many more peppers were there than beets?

   Ⓕ 1   Ⓗ 32

   Ⓖ 3   Ⓐ 5

Explore Regrouping

Play a regrouping game with a partner. Cut out the number cards below. The I-digit numbers are tens. The 2-digit numbers are ones. Separate them into two stacks. Mix up each set of cards and put them facedown.

How to Play

- Take turns with your partner.

- Players I and 2: Choose one card from each stack.

- Regroup the ones and write the total of your two numbers.

- Players I and 2 compare numbers.

- The player with the higher number gets I point. Repeat.

- Put your cards back in the stacks and mix them up.

The first player to get I0 points wins.

1	2	3	4	5	6
7	8	9	18	33	27
45	16	13	22	37	33

1	2	3	4	5	6
7	8	9	18	33	27
45	16	13	22	37	33

Use with Grade 2, Chapter 12, Lesson 1, pages 209–210.

Addition with Sums to 20

Play an addition game with a partner. Cut out the spinner.
Use a pencil and paper clip to spin the spinner.

How to Play

- Take turns, beginning with Player 1.

- Spin the spinner. Record the number you land on. Repeat.
  Add the two numbers. Do this until you reach or go over 20.
  Count how many spins it took for you to reach 20.

- Player 2 repeats the steps outlined above.

- Players 1 and 2 compare notes. The player who reached
  20 with fewest spins gets a point.

- Repeat.

The player who gets
10 points wins.

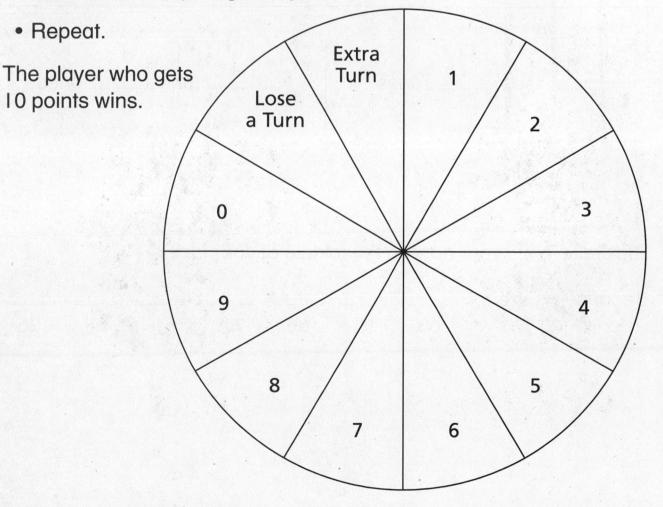

Addition with Greater Numbers

Regroup to find each sum. Tell how many tens and
ones. Fill in the letters below to solve the riddle.

1.   24 + 17

_____ tens _____ ones

24 + 17 = _____   C

2.   36 + 28

_____ tens _____ ones

36 + 28 = _____   E

3.   18 + 44

_____ tens _____ ones

18 + 44 = _____   N

4.   27 + 19

_____ tens _____ ones

27 + 19 = _____   R

5.   48 + 15

_____ tens _____ ones

48 + 15 = _____   S

6.   14 + 37

_____ tens _____ ones

14 + 37 = _____   T

Riddle: Why is your nose in the middle of your face?

Because it's the   ___ ___ ___   ___ ___ ___ ___
                    63   41   64   62   51   64   46

Use with Grade 2, Chapter 12, Lesson 3, pages 213–214.

Renaming Numbers

Play a renaming game with a partner.

How to Play

- One player drops a coin or counter on the game board below.

- Both players have 30 seconds to write down ways to name that number.

- Compare answers. Each correct name for the number gets one point.

- Repeat

The first player to reach 25 points wins the game.

28	35	17	38
62	83	17	49
18	25	62	41
32	67	19	31

Add Tens

E 13-1 **ENRICH**

Circle the missing tens.

1.
```
  30    10
+ ▩     20
  50    30
```

2.
```
  30    40
+ ▩     30
  60    20
```

3.
```
  20    60
+ ▩     70
  90    80
```

4.
```
  50    20
+ ▩     30
  70    40
```

5.
```
  50    30
+ ▩     40
  80    50
```

6.
```
  60    30
+ ▩     20
  70    10
```

7.
```
  40    50
+ ▩     60
  90    70
```

8.
```
  20    50
+ ▩     60
  80    70
```

9.
```
  40    60
+ ▩     50
  80    40
```

10.
```
  60    30
+ ▩     40
  90    50
```

11.
```
  10    80
+ ▩     70
  90    60
```

12.
```
  40    30
+ ▩     20
  60    10
```

Add across. Add down. Find the missing tens.

13.

10		30
	10	
20		50

20		40
	20	
40		80

30		60
	30	
30		90

Use with Grade 2, Chapter 13, Lesson 1, pages 231–232.

Count on Tens and Ones to Add

Count on by tens and ones to solve each riddle.

1. I am a 2-digit number ending in 6. If you begin with 16 and count on by 7 tens, you will find me. What am I? _____

2. I am a number whose last digit is 6. Begin with 21. Count on by 5 ones. What am I? _____

3. Both my digits are the same. Count on from 37 by 4 tens. What am I? _____

4. I am the number of tens you need to count on to add 53 + 40. What am I? _____

5. I am the number of ones you need to count on to add 64 + 5. What am I? _____

6. I am the number of tens you need to count on from 28 to get 98. What am I? _____

7. You began with 42 and used me to reach 46. I am the number of ones you counted on. What am I? _____

8. You began with 28. You counted on 4 tens to reach me. What am I? _____

9. Write your own number riddle on the lines below. Then trade papers with a classmate and solve each other's riddles.

_____

_____

_____

_____

Decide When to Regroup

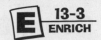
Add. Color the addition problems that need regrouping.

Find the path through the maze.

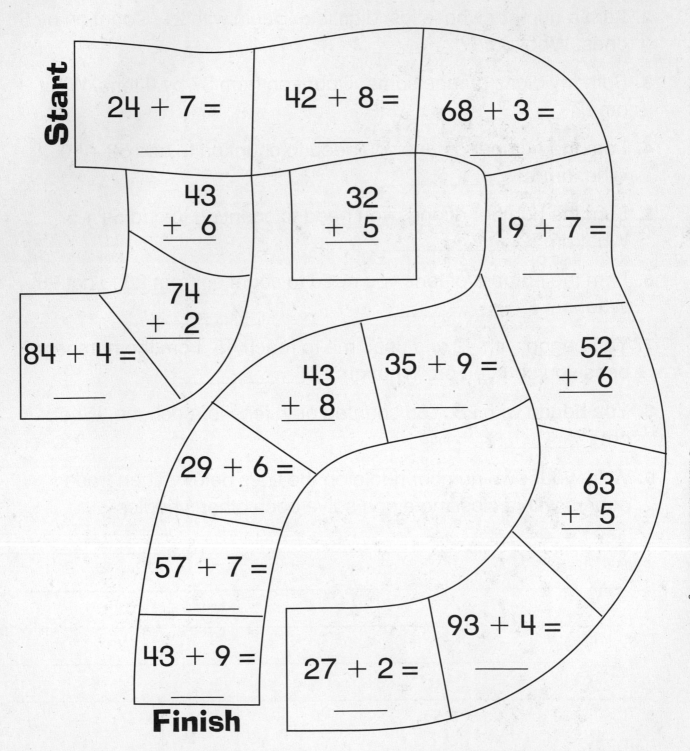

Start

24 + 7 = _____

42 + 8 = _____

68 + 3 = _____

43
+ 6
____

32
+ 5
____

19 + 7 = _____

74
+ 2
____

84 + 4 = _____

43
+ 8
____

35 + 9 = _____

52
+ 6
____

29 + 6 = _____

63
+ 5
____

57 + 7 = _____

43 + 9 = _____

27 + 2 = _____

93 + 4 = _____

Finish

Use with Grade 2, Chapter 13, Lesson 3, pages 237–238.

Add a 1-Digit and a 2-Digit Number

Use the numbers in the boxes to write
two different addition sentences.

You may use a number more than once.

1.

5	3	26
20	23	28

_23_ + _5_ = _28_

_23_ + _3_ = _26_

2.

7	6	48
42	58	65

____ + ____ = ____

____ + ____ = ____

3.

9	19	15
39	4	48

____ + ____ = ____

____ + ____ = ____

4.

2	73	71
8	19	11

____ + ____ = ____

____ + ____ = ____

5.

5	3	57
52	90	87

____ + ____ = ____

____ + ____ = ____

Add 2-Digit Numbers

Play with a partner. Take turns.

How to Play

• Drop a coin on the game board two times. You have two numbers.

• Add the numbers on a separate sheet of paper.

• The person with the greater sum gets 1 point. Repeat.

The person who gets 10 points first wins the game.

Scoring Chart	
Name	Points

14	37	52	38
25	46	17	21
43	33	28	39
27	11	42	30
65	27	92	86

Use with Grade 2, Chapter 13, Lesson 5, pages 241–242.

Practice Addition

Each row of numbers is in a pattern.

Find the next number in the pattern.

Circle the rule.

Which is the rule?			
+ 8 + 9	16	24	32	_____
+ 13 + 14	26	39	52	_____
+ 16 + 17	27	44	61	_____
+ 23 + 24	27	51	75	_____
+ 11 + 12	32	43	54	_____
+ 25 + 30	15	40	65	_____

Name _____

Problem Solving Skill: Reading For Math

Problem and Solution

Solve.

1. Terry and Aaron are putting on a play. There are parts for 14 boys and 16 girls. How many actors do they need?

   _____

2. Sita made most of the costumes. She needs to buy the rest. She will have to buy 25 hats and 18 wigs. How many hats and wigs must she buy in all?

   _____

3. Tom has to learn 63 lines for his part. Ming has to learn 28 lines for his part. How many lines do they have to learn in all?

   _____

4. Act One of the play is 45 minutes long. Act Two is 38 minutes long. How long is the whole play?

   _____

5. Some audience members will sit on benches. Small children will sit on the floor in front. The benches will hold 45 people. There is room on the floor for 44 children. How many people can see the play?

   _____

6. Shelia will sell drinks and snacks at intermission. Cookies cost 15¢ each. Drinks cost 45¢ each. How much does it cost to buy one drink and one cookie?

   _____

7. Choose a partner. Work together to write a story like the one above. Include a sum for each part of the story. Use separate sheets of paper.

   _____

   _____

Use with Grade 2, Chapter 13, Lesson 7, pages 245–246.

Rewrite Addition

Play a game with a partner.

How to Play

• Toss two coins or counters onto the board.

• Write the two numbers the coins land on as an addition problem.

• Solve the problem.

• Check your answer. If it's correct, you get one point. If it's wrong, you lose a turn.

Take turns with your partner. The first player to get 5 points wins.

56	18	45	72
38	91	13	24
23	27	54	62
31	17	49	82

Practice 2-Digit Addition

Find the missing number.

I have a 9 in the ones place. When you add 26 to me, you get 45. What number am I?

```
  9
+ 26
 45
```
_____

---

1. I have a 2 in the tens place. When you add 18 to me, you get 39. What number am I?

_____

2. I have a 5 in the ones place. When you add 30 to me, you get 55. What number am I?

_____

---

3. My tens digit and my ones digit are the same number. When you add 42 to me, you get 75. What number am I?

_____

4. My ones digit is 5 greater than my tens digit. When you add 16 to me, you get 43. What number am I?

_____

---

5. My tens digit is 3 less than my ones digit. When you add 52 to me, you get 66. What number am I?

_____

6. My tens digit and my ones digit are even numbers. When you add 33 to me, you get 77. What number am I?

_____

---

7. Write your own missing number riddle. Solve it. Then give it to a classmate to solve.

_____

_____

Use with Grade 2, Chapter 14, Lesson 2, pages 255–256.

Check Addition • Algebra

Circle two pairs of numbers with the same sum.

Then find all sums.

1. 27 + 54 ____   18 + 47 ____   55 + 21 ____

21 + 55 ____   54 + 37 ____   37 + 18 ____

_____

2. 34 + 61 ____   45 + 16 ____   62 + 11 ____

16 + 35 ____   11 + 52 ____   61 + 34 ____

_____

3. 29 + 46 ____   64 + 28 ____   44 + 29 ____

18 + 64 ____   46 + 29 ____   36 + 44 ____

_____

4. 27 + 19 ____   39 + 38 ____   19 + 29 ____

38 + 39 ____   45 + 37 ____   37 + 54 ____

_____

How do you know the number pairs have the same sum?

_____

_____

Estimate Sums

Mr. Marvin's class collected bottles for recycling.

The chart shows how many bottles each child collected.
Estimate how many bottles each pair collected.

Jackson 34	Marie 49	Jamal 52	Keesha 18
Kenny 51	Paco 27	Paula 38	Maura 43

1. About how many bottles did Jackson and Jamal collect?

about _____ bottles

2. About how many bottles did Marie and Maura collect?

about _____ bottles

3. About how many bottles did Keesha and Kenny collect?

about _____ bottles

4. About how many bottles did Paula and Paco collect?

about _____ bottles

Three of the children collected about 100 bottles in all.
Who are the three children?

_____

_____

Add Three Numbers

Play a game with a partner. Take turns.

How to Play

• Drop a coin on the target below.

• Add the three numbers in the section where the coin lands.

• Play three rounds.

Add up the three sums on your paper. That number is your score.

The player with the greater number of points is the winner.

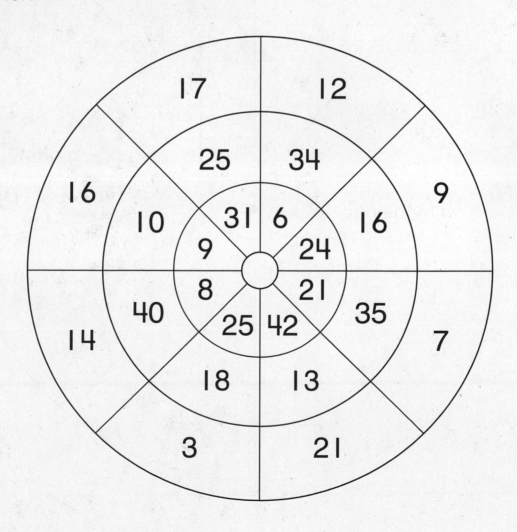

Subtract Tens

Drop a coin on the target twice. Subtract the lesser
number from the greater.
If the difference is 50 or greater, you get 1 point.
If the difference is less than 50, you get 2 points.
Take turns with a partner.
The first player to reach 10 points wins.

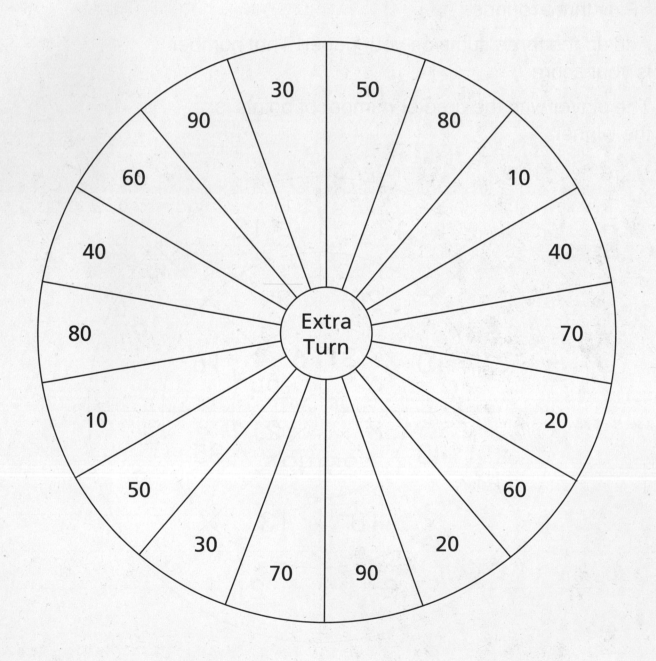

Count Back Tens and Ones to Subtract

Count back by tens and ones to solve each riddle.

1. I am a two-digit number ending in 6. If you begin with 76 and count back by 2 tens, you will find me. What am I? _____

2. I am a one-digit number. Begin with 51. Count back by 5 tens. What am I? _____

3. Count back from 37 by 2 tens and 5 ones. You will find me. What am I? _____

4. I am the number of tens you need to count back to subtract $68 - 40$. What am I? _____

5. I am the number of ones you need to count back to subtract $59 - 5$. What am I? _____

6. I am the number of tens you need to count back from 98 to get 38. What am I? _____

7. I am the number of ones you counted back. You began with 47 and used me to reach 41. What am I? _____

8. You began with 67. You counted back 4 tens to reach me. What am I? _____

9. Write your own subtraction riddle on the lines below. Then trade papers with a classmate and solve each other's riddles.

_____

_____

_____

_____

Decide When to Regroup

Play with a partner. Take turns.

- Drop a counter on the game board. Subtract.
- Score one point if you need to regroup.
- Score one point for a correct answer.

Scoring Chart	
Name	Points

The first player to reach 10 points is the winner.

Game Board

57 − 9	24 − 6	37 − 5	88 − 3
45 − 7	67 − 4	39 − 6	80 − 5
18 − 2	27 − 8	46 − 7	53 − 1
55 − 6	79 − 4	92 − 8	66 − 6
97 − 3	62 − 9	31 − 6	72 − 5

With your partner, write a rule that tells when you need to regroup.

_____

Use with Grade 2, Chapter 15, Lesson 3, pages 277–278.

Subtract a 1-Digit Number from a 2-Digit Number

Play a subtraction game. Cut out the cards below.

Mix them up. Put them facedown on a table.

How to Play

- Take turns with a partner.
- Pick a card. Subtract. Check your answer.
- If your answer is correct, move the number of spaces shown in the circle on the card. Use a counter.

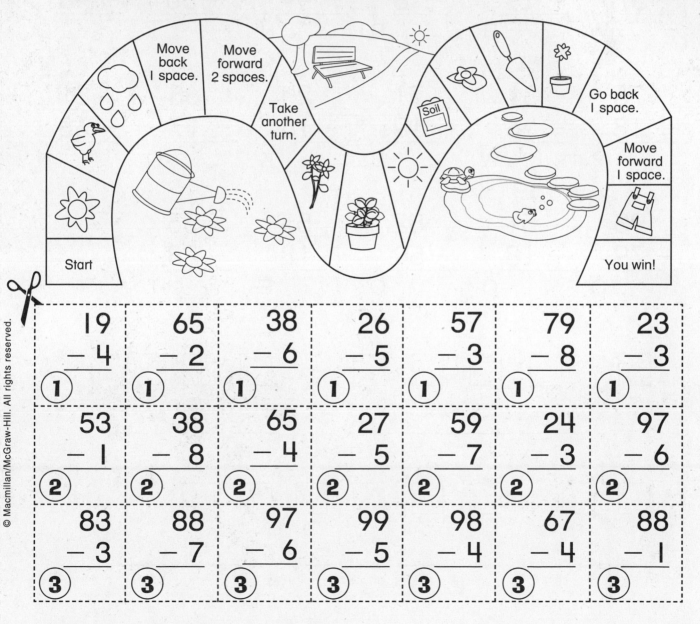

Subtract 2-Digit Numbers

Subtract to find the differences.

Then put them in order from least to greatest in the boxes below.

Look at the letter next to the answer.

Write the letters on the lines under the differences.
Read the secret message.

53	64	44	71	43	92
− 37	− 19	− 8	− 49	− 38	− 48
W	R	R	H	I	G

75	31	71	24	65	81
− 18	− 6	− 19	− 15	− 17	− 68
P	W	U	K	O	N

93	51	82	55	56
− 79	− 18	− 59	− 18	− 28
O	O	O	E	T

☐5 ☐ ☐ ☐ ☐   ☐ ☐ ☐
 I __ __ __ __   __ __ __

☐ ☐ ☐ ☐ ☐ ☐ ☐ ☐ ☐
__ __ __ __ __ __ __ __ __

Use with Grade 2, Chapter 15, Lesson 5, pages 281–282.

Practice Subtraction

Subtract. Follow the differences from greatest to least.

Trace the path from Start to the Fountain.

Start

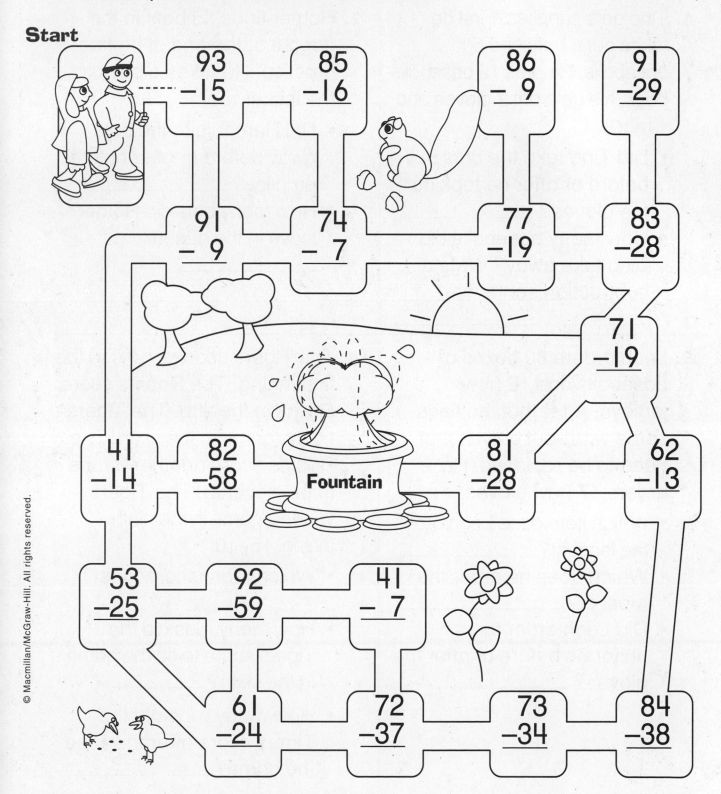

Problem Solving Skill: Reading for Math
Sequence of Events

E 15-7 ENRICH

Solve.

1. Tino gets supplies. First he takes out 6 bats and 50 baseballs. He puts 15 baseballs back. He gets out 2 gloves and 1 mask.

- Did Tino take the bats out before or after he took out the gloves? _____
- How many baseballs did Tino take away? Write a subtraction sentence.

_____

2. Homer finds 35 bats in the dugout at the end of batting practice. He takes 6 back to the locker room.

- Did Homer take the bats away before or after batting practice? _____
- How many bats did Homer leave in the dugout?

_____

3. Leon orders 80 boxes of baseballs and 12 new jerseys. After that, he finds some worn-out gloves that need to be replaced. He orders 17 new gloves.

- Which item does Leon order the least of? _____
- Which does he order the most of? _____
- Did Leon order the uniforms before or after the gloves? _____

4. The Tigers score 2 runs in the first inning. The Robins score 5 runs in the fifth. The Tigers tie the game in the sixth. The Robins score another 3 runs in the seventh. The Tigers win the game in the ninth inning, 15–10.

- Which team scored first?

_____

- How many runs did the Tigers score to tie the game in the sixth? _____
- How many runs did the Tigers score after they tied the game? _____

Use with Grade 2, Chapter 15, Lesson 7, pages 285–286.

Rewrite 2-Digit Subtraction

Riddle: What is in the middle of America?

To find the answer, rewrite and then solve each subtraction problem. Fill in the correct letter next to each answer below.

1. $62 - 35 =$ _____   **A**

2. $27 - 8 =$ _____   **E**

3. $43 - 17 =$ _____   **H**

4. $81 - 34 =$ _____   **L**

5. $38 - 29 =$ _____   **R**

6. $52 - 48 =$ _____   **T**

___ ___ ___
4   26   19

___ ___ ___ ___ ___ ___
47   19   4   4   19   9

___
9

Practice 2-Digit Subtraction

Play this game with a partner.

- Drop a coin twice on the target.

- Subtract the lesser number from the greater number.

- Each correct answer is worth 1 point.

The first player to get 10 points wins.

Scoring Chart	
Name	Points

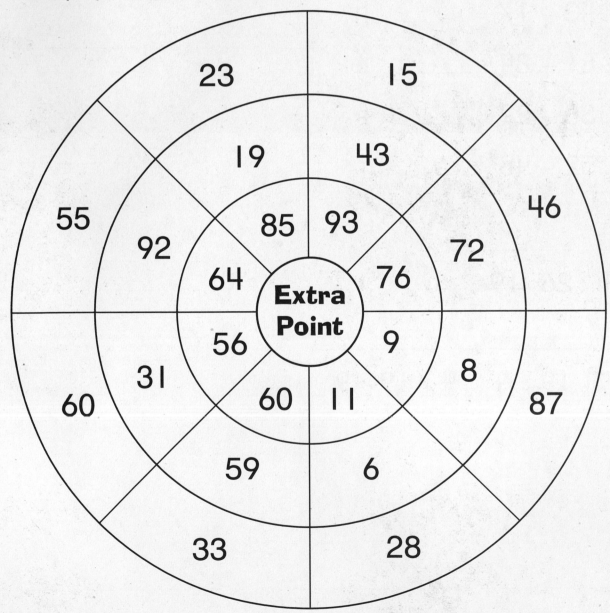

Use with Grade 2, Chapter 16, Lesson 2, pages 295–296.

Check Subtraction

Read the chart kept by the Bird-Watchers Club.

Birds We Saw in May				
Blue Jays	Sparrows	Robins	Cardinals	Wrens
61	45	37	52	18

Solve and check your answers.

	Subtract	**Check**
1. How many more cardinals were seen than sparrows? _____ cardinals	52 − 45	+ 45
2. How many more blue jays were seen than robins? _____ blue jays	61 − 37	+ 37
3. How many more cardinals were seen than wrens? _____ cardinals	52 − 18	+ 18
4. In June, 85 blue jays were spotted. How many more blue jays were spotted in June than in May? _____ blue jays	85 − 61	+ 61

Name _____

Estimate Differences

 16-4 ENRICH

Make a giant butterfly.

Estimate each difference.

Color estimates of 10 through 50)))) orange))) .

Color estimates of 60 through 90)))) yellow))) .

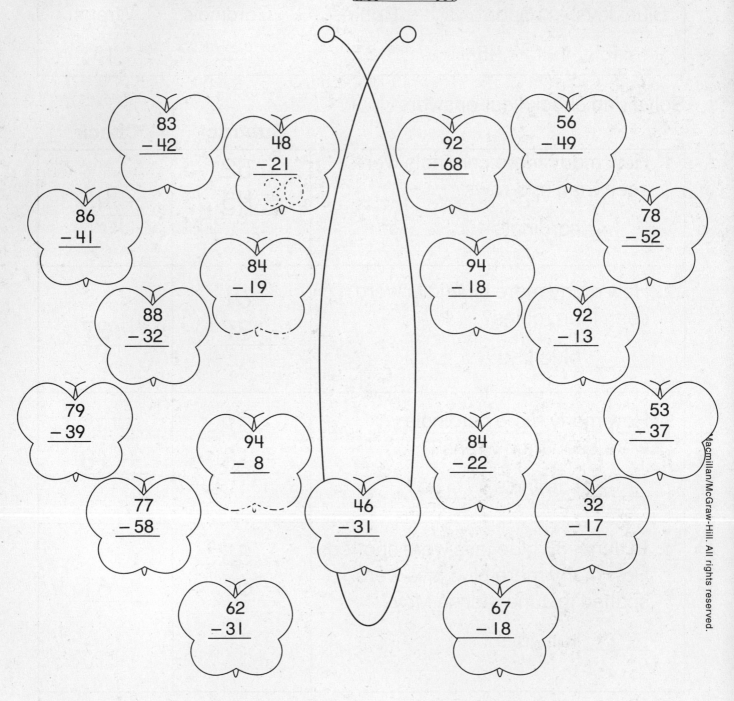

$$83 - 42$$

$$48 - 21$$ (30)

$$92 - 68$$

$$56 - 49$$

$$86 - 41$$

$$84 - 19$$

$$94 - 18$$

$$78 - 52$$

$$88 - 32$$

$$92 - 13$$

$$79 - 39$$

$$94 - 8$$

$$84 - 22$$

$$53 - 37$$

$$77 - 58$$

$$46 - 31$$

$$32 - 17$$

$$62 - 31$$

$$67 - 18$$

Use with Grade 2, Chapter 16, Lesson 4, pages 299–300.

Mental Math: Strategies

Play a game with a partner.
Cut out and mix up the number cards below.

- Choose two cards.
- Player 1 subtracts the lesser number from the greater.
- Player 2 adds the two numbers.

Use mental math to add and subtract.
Each correct answer is worth one point.
The first player to reach 10 is the winner.

✂

25	42	33	12	58
38	29	18	44	51
82	72	95	33	21
47	36	66	23	41
22	19	67	88	39
77	29	13	94	59

Nonstandard Units of Length

Find the objects below in your classroom.

Use to measure the objects.

1.

How wide is the book?   Estimate _____   measure _____

2.

How long is the notebook?   Estimate _____   measure _____

3.

How tall is the milk carton?   Estimate _____   measure _____

4.

How long is the leg of the chair?

Estimate _____   measure _____

Use with Grade 2, Chapter 17, Lesson 1, pages 317–318.

Measure to the Nearest Inch

Play a measuring game with a partner. Cut out the cards at the bottom of the page. Mix them up. Take turns.

How to Play

• Each player chooses one card and measures the object named or shown. Use an inch ruler. Measure the length.

• Players then compare measures. The object measuring fewer inches gets one point.

• Put the cards back in the pile. Mix them up again. Continue playing.

The first player to get 10 points wins.

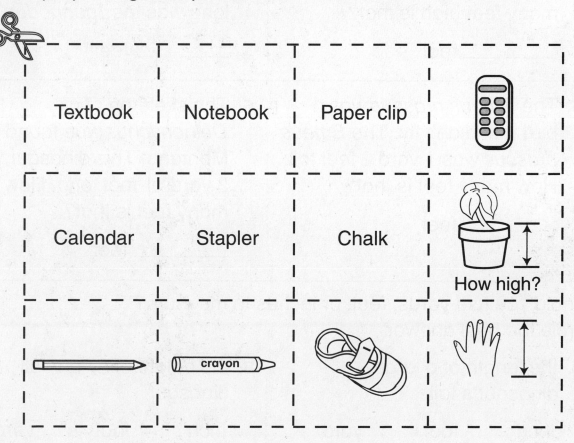

Textbook	Notebook	Paper clip	
Calendar	Stapler	Chalk	How high?
	crayon		

Name _____

Inch, Foot, and Yard

Complete the chart.

Yards	1	2	3	4	5	6
Feet	3		9			

Use the chart to answer each question.

1. A scientist found a dinosaur nest that was about 9 feet long. How many yards is that?

_____ yards

2. The head of an *Allosaurus* was about 3 feet long. How many yards is that?

_____ yard

3. A *Tyrannosaurus rex* stood about 6 yards high. How many feet high is that?

_____ feet

4. An *Iguanodon* was about 10 yards long. How many feet long was the *Iguanodon*?

_____ feet

5. The *Emeus crassus* was a bird that didn't fly. The *Emeus crassus* was 1 yard 2 feet tall. How many feet is that?

_____ feet

6. The skeleton of a *Deinonychus* was found in Montana. This dinosaur was 3 yards 1 foot long. How many feet is that?

_____ feet

Would you use yards, feet, or inches to measure?
Circle the best answer.

7. the length of a large dinosaur's tail

inch   foot   yard

8. the height of a very tall dinosaur

inch   foot   yard

Use with Grade 2, Chapter 17, Lesson 3, pages 321–322.

Centimeter and Meter

Complete. Go on a scavenger hunt.

1. Find something that has the length shown. Measure with a centimeter ruler. Draw pictures.

5 centimeters	10 centimeters
20 centimeters	50 centimeters

2. Find something that is about 1 meter long. Measure it with a meterstick. Draw a picture of it.

3. Would you use centimeters or meters to measure the length of a playground? Explain your answer.

_____

_____

Name_____

Problem Solving Skill: Reading for Math
Compare and Contrast

1. Jim is 4 feet tall. Tony is 40 inches tall. Sara is 4 feet 3 inches tall. Write the children's heights from shortest to tallest.

   _____

2. Karen is 30 inches tall. Sally is 22 inches tall. Gayden is 28 inches tall. Are any of them more than 2 feet tall? Which ones?

   _____

3. Jim's cat is 25 inches long from nose to tail. Sara's cat is 28 inches long. Tony's cat is 30 inches long. How long is each cat in both feet and inches?

   _____

   _____

4. Jim's mom is 5 feet 8 inches tall. Sara's mom is 5 feet 5 inches. Gayden's mom is 5 feet 3 inches. How tall is each mom in inches?

   _____

   _____

5. Karen's dog is 1 yard tall and Tony's dog is 2 feet 6 inches tall. How many inches tall is each dog? Which dog is taller?

   _____

   _____

Use with Grade 2, Chapter 17, Lesson 5, pages 325–326.

Explore Capacity

You can measure capacity in different ways. You can use a milk carton to measure capacity.

The milk carton holds **less** than the pitcher.

The pitcher will hold about 2 containers of milk.

MILK + MILK =

Tell about how many of the smaller containers the larger container will hold.

1.

_____ containers

2.

_____ containers

3.

_____ containers

Name _____

Fluid Ounce, Cup, Pint, Quart, and Gallon

Amanda is making fruit punch.

Use the recipe to solve. Put a ✓ by each answer.

1. How many fluid ounces of orange juice does Amanda need for the punch?

_____ 8 fl oz

_____ 16 fl oz

_____ 32 fl oz

2. Amanda wants to make 2 batches of punch. How many cups of yogurt does she need?

_____ 2 cups

_____ 4 cups

_____ 6 cups

3. How many pints of strawberries does Amanda need for the punch?

_____ 1 pint

_____ 2 pints

_____ 4 pints

4. How many quarts of orange juice does Amanda need if she wants to make at least a gallon of punch?

_____ 4 quarts

_____ 6 quarts

_____ 12 quarts

Use with Grade 2, Chapter 18, Lesson 2, pages 335–336.

Ounce and Pound

Balance the scale.
Tell how many of each fruit you need.

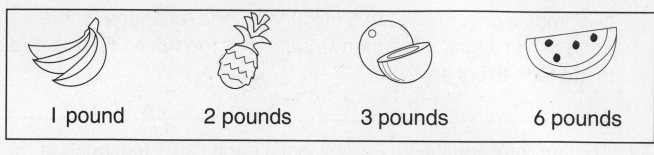

I pound	2 pounds	3 pounds	6 pounds

1.

_____

2.

_____

3.

_____

4.

_____

5. A  and a are on the left side of a balanced scale. There are two kinds of fruit on the right side of the scale. How many of each kind of fruit are on the right side?

_____ and _____

Name_____

Milliliter and Liter

Solve each problem.

1. Franny runs a pet store. She feeds each fish 1 teaspoon of food two times a day. There are 5 milliliters in one teaspoon. There are 3 fish in a tank. How many milliliters of food does Franny add to the tank every day?

_____

2. Another tank has 4 fish. Franny feeds each fish 1 teaspoon of food three times a day. How many milliliters of food does she add to the tank each day?

_____

3. The biggest fish tank in the store holds 50 liters of water. About how many of each container would Franny need to fill up the tank?

_____

_____

_____

Use with Grade 2, Chapter 18, Lesson 4, pages 339–340.

Name _____

Gram and Kilogram

18-5 ENRICH

potatoes
8 kg

apples
5 kg

tomatoes
3 kg

turkey
9 kg

watermelon
6 kg

bananas
2 kg

1. Miss Mark has a shopping bag that holds up to 15 kg. Which 3 things can she buy?

_____

2. Mr. Lee has a shopping cart that holds up to 30 kg. He buys 2 packages of turkey. How many baskets of tomatoes can he buy?

_____

3. Ms. Flockhart has a shopping bag that holds up to 20 kg. She buys 2 baskets of apples. Which other 2 things can she buy?

_____

Would you use grams or kilograms to measure?
Circle the better answer.

4. the mass of an apple

grams   kilograms

the mass of a shopping cart

grams   kilograms

Temperature

Find a newspaper. Look up the high temperature for the day.

Color the temperature on the thermometer for 4 days.

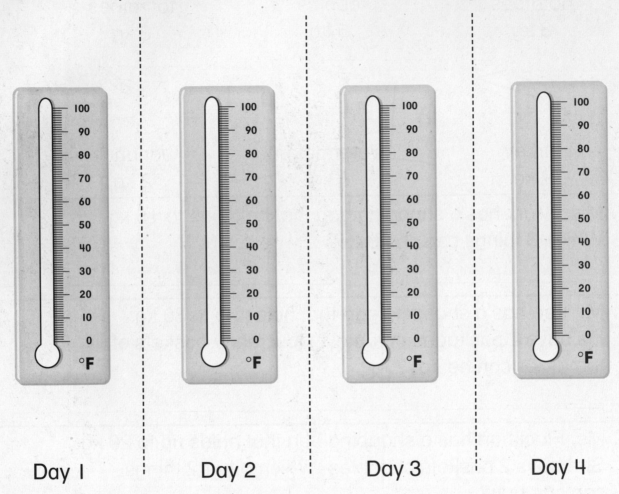

Day 1   Day 2   Day 3   Day 4

Use your thermometers to answer each question.

1. On what day was the temperature the warmest? _____

2. On what day was the temperature the coolest? _____

3. What is the difference in temperature between the warmest day and the coolest day? _____

Use with Grade 2, Chapter 18, Lesson 6, pages 343–344.

3-Dimensional Figures

Cut out the shapes. Fold along the dotted
lines to make a solid figure.

Write the name of the solid figure.
Choose from the list.

cone

cube

cylinder

pyramid

rectangular prism

1.

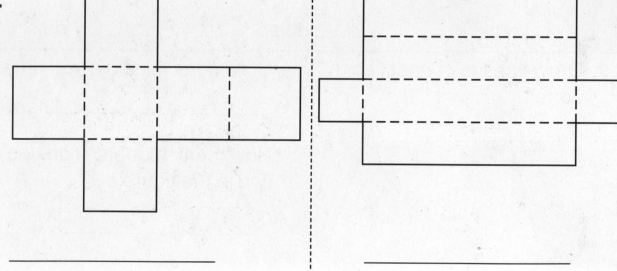

_____   _____

2.

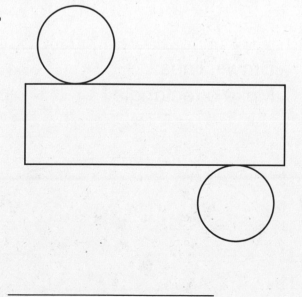

_____   _____

2-Dimensional Shapes

1. Look at the dot pattern. Draw the next quadrilateral. Write how many dots in each.

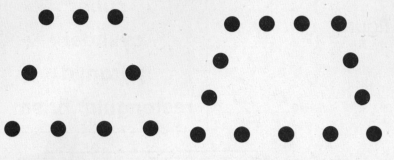

_____ dots   _____ dots   _____ dots

2. Draw lines to connect each vertex.

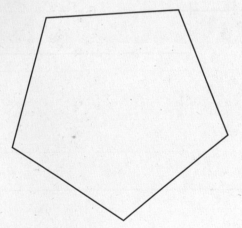

How many lines did you draw?

_____ lines

How many triangles can you find in the figure?

_____

3. Draw 2 lines.
Make 2 triangles and 1 rectangle.

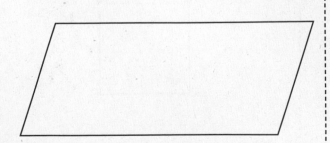

Draw 4 lines.
Make a rectangle

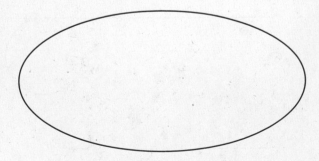

2-Dimensional and 3-Dimensional Relationships

Play a game with a partner. Cut out the cards shown below. Mix up the cards. Divide them between you.

How to Play

- Look at the 3-dimensional figures at right. Look at your cards. Do you have enough shapes to make one of the 3-dimensional figures?

- If you can make one of the figures, you get one point. Mix up the cards and play again.

  Hint: The card with the tallest rectangle can be used with two other shapes to make a cylinder.

cube	
rectangular prism	
cylinder	
pyramid	

Play 5 times. The player with the most points wins.

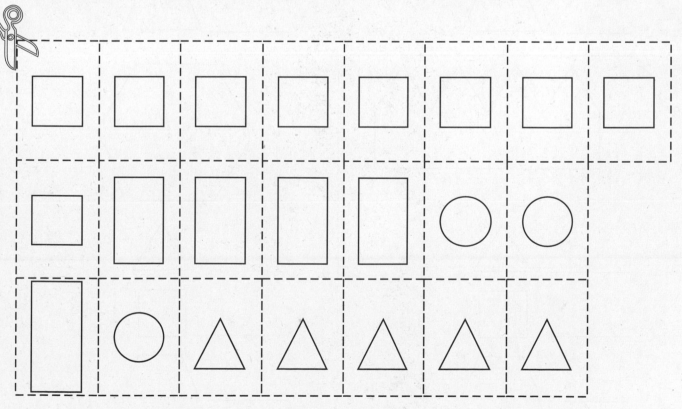

Combine Shapes

Use pattern blocks to make each shape.
Write how many of each kind of block you use.

1.

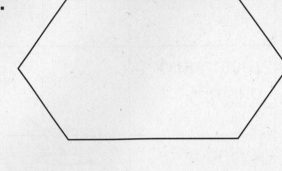

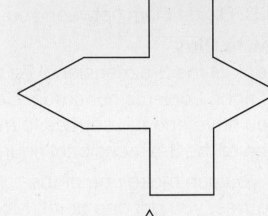

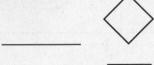

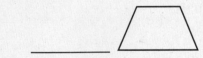

2.

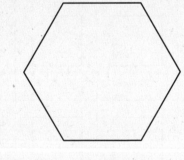

Use with Grade 2, Chapter 19, Lesson 4, pages 359–360.

Shape Patterns

Complete each pattern. Write the name of each shape you use.

1. ⬡ ○ △ ▢ ▢ ○ △ ▢ _____

_____

2. ✳ ◇ ✳ ◇ ✳ ◇ _____

_____

3. 🏠 🏠 🏠 🏠 _____

_____

4. _____

_____

Problem Solving Skill: Reading for Math
Use Illustrations

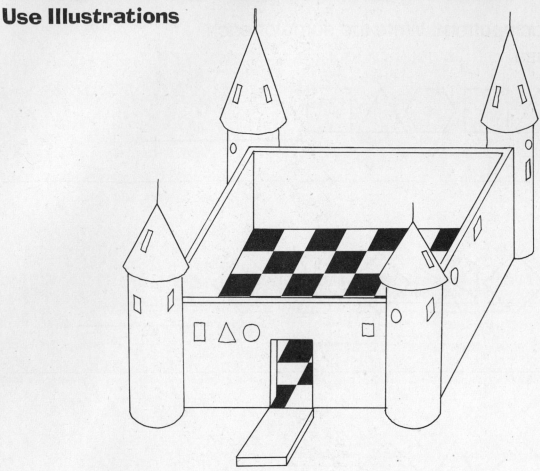

Look at the illustration of a castle. Complete.

1. How would you describe the castle's towers?

_____

_____

2. What shapes are used in the pattern of the floor?

_____

_____

3. Draw a flag flying from each flag pole on the castle's four towers. What shapes are your flags?

_____

_____

4. Draw and name the 2-dimensional and 3-dimensional figures you see in the castle.

_____

_____

Congruence

Circle the shape that is congruent
to the given part of this solid.

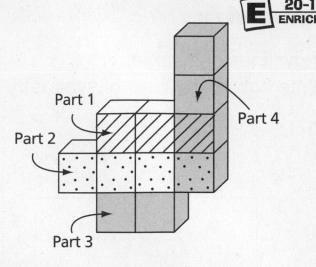

Part 1

Part 2

Part 4

Part 3

1. Part 1

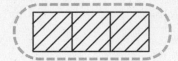

2. Part 2

3. Part 3

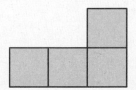

4. Part 4

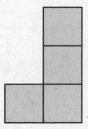

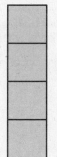

Symmetry

Draw lines of symmetry.
Write how many lines of symmetry for each shape.

1.

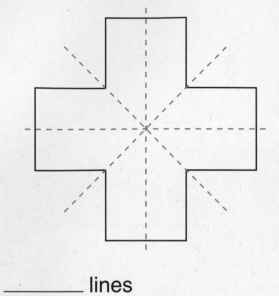

_____ lines

2.

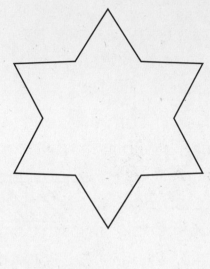

_____ lines

3.

_____ lines

4.

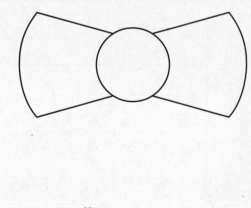

_____ lines

5. Write your name in capital letters.
Find letters with a line of symmetry. Draw the lines.

_____

_____

Name_____

Slides, Flips, and Turns

Play a game with a partner. Cut out the three word cards. Cut out the shape cards numbered 1–5. The other shape cards (6–10) form a game board.

How to Play

Mix up and place the word cards face down. Place shape cards numbered 1–5 face up.

- Player 1: Turn over one word card. Player 2: Choose one shape card. Match it with its mate on the game board using a slide, flip, or turn. The dots on the the 2 shapes should coincide. Switch roles and repeat.
- Give one point for each correct answer.

The first player to reach 5 points wins.

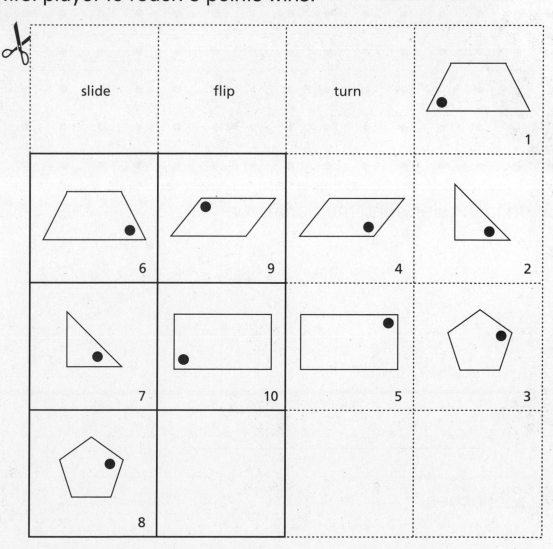

Use with Grade 2, Chapter 20, Lesson 3, pages 377–378.

Perimeter

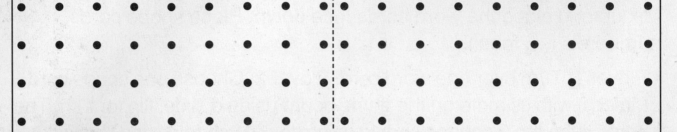

1. Draw a shape with a perimeter of 6 units.

Draw a shape with a perimeter of 10 units.

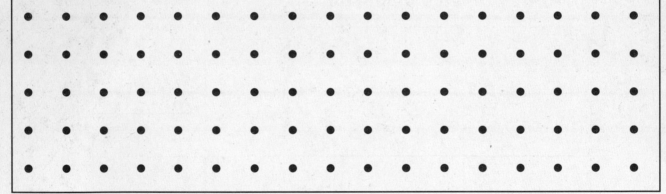

2. Draw a shape with a perimeter of 16 units.

3. Use an inch ruler. Find the perimeter.

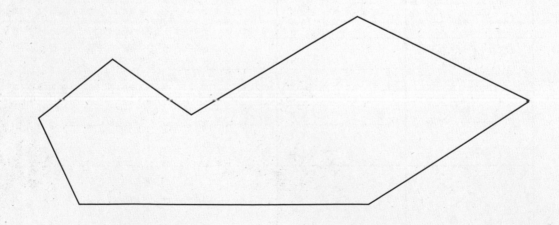

_____ inches

Use with Grade 2, Chapter 20, Lesson 4, pages 379–380.

Area

Count the number of square units in the shaded figure.

1.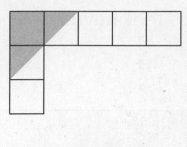

_____ square units

2.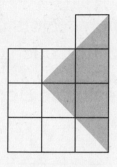

_____ square units

3.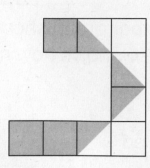

_____ square units

4.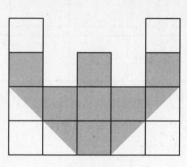

_____ square units

5.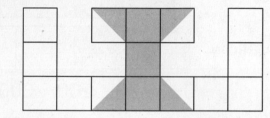

_____ square units

6. Draw a shape.
How many square units
are in the shape?

_____ square units

7. Color some of the squares.
How many square units did
you color?

_____ square units

Hundreds

Members of the Crafts Club are making necklaces.

The bar graph shows how many colors of beads they have.
It also shows how many beads of each color.

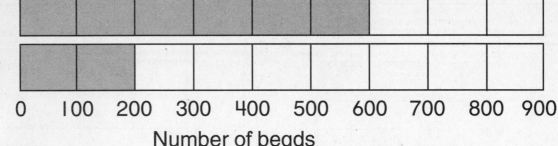

1. How many blue beads are there? _____

2. How many yellow beads are there? _____

3. How many red beads are there? _____

4. How many green beads are there? _____

5. Write out the number of each color of bead in words.

red _____   blue _____

green _____   yellow _____

Use with Grade 2, Chapter 21, Lesson 1, pages 397–398.

Hundreds, Tens, and Ones

Max likes to play Bull's-Eye. Each dart shows a hit.

Write the points for each game.

1.

300 + 40 + 2

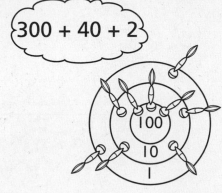

_____ points

2.

_____ points

3.

_____ points

4.

_____ points

5.

_____ points

6.

_____ points

Name _____

Place Value Through Hundreds

Read the story. Then answer each question.

Pearl Street School held a crafts fair. There were 200 + 40 + 7 students at the fair. Each booth sold different things. The first grade class used 100 + 90 + 3 strings to make pot holders. The second grade used 600 + 50 + 1 beads to make necklaces. The third grade used 400 + 20 + 8 pieces of yarn to make puppets. There were 100 + 20 + 6 parents at the fair. There were 700 + 80 + 3 cups of juice sold at the fair. Everyone had a good time.

1. How many pieces of yarn did the third grade use?

_____ pieces

2. How many students were at the fair? _____ students

3. How many pieces of string did the first grade use?

_____ pieces

4. How many parents were at the fair? _____ parents

5. How many cups of juice were sold? _____ cups

6. How many beads did the second grade use?

_____ beads

Use with Grade 2, Chapter 21, Lesson 3, pages 401–402.

Explore Place Value to Thousands

Play a game. Choose a partner. Cut out and combine two sets of number cards.

How to Play

• Mix up the cards and spread them out facedown.

• Choose four cards. Turn them right side up to form a 4-digit number. Remember that 0 cannot be the first digit.

• Write how many thousands, hundreds, tens, and ones.

• Each correct answer gets 2 points.

• Take turns with your partner.

The first player to get 10 points wins.

Number Card

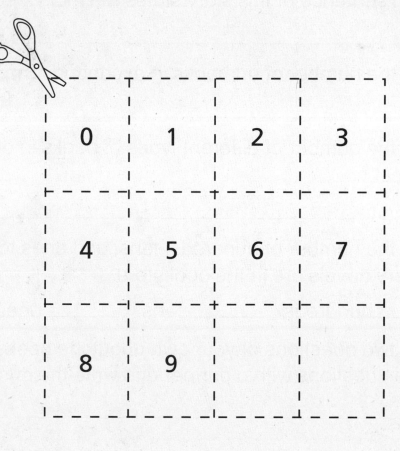

Name_____

Problem Solving Skill: Reading for Math
Find the Main Idea

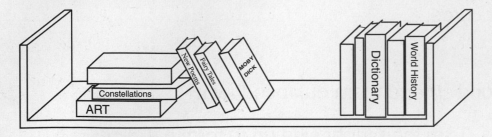

Read the story.

Stephanie and Jamal run a bookstore. They have 925 mystery novels in one section. They have 650 history books in another. They have 863 children's books, 403 books of poetry, and 230 science books against the back wall. The big art books take up the most space. There are 550 of these.

1. Which sentence of this story states the main idea?

_____

2. Write the number of art books in expanded form.

_____

3. Write the number of different types of books in order from least to greatest.

_____

4. Write the number of hundreds, tens, and ones to show how many mystery novels are in the bookstore.

_____ hundreds _____ tens _____ ones

5. Write two questions of your own about the books in the store. Trade questions with a partner and write the answers.

_____

_____

Use with Grade 2, Chapter 21, Lesson 5, pages 407–408.

Compare Numbers • Algebra

Play a game with a partner.

How to Play

- Each player tosses a counter on the game board.

- The players compare the numbers they land on.

- The player with the greater number gets 1 point.

The first player to reach 10 points wins.

Scoring Chart	
Name	Points

3 ones 4 tens 2 hundreds	500 + 60 + 7	(base-ten blocks)	**H T O** 4 3 1
600 + 30 + 0	(base-ten blocks)	5 ones 6 tens 3 hundreds	**H T O** 9 5 2
(base-ten blocks)	**H T O** 6 7 4	100 + 70 + 9	5 ones 9 tens 9 hundreds
800 + 60 + 3	7 ones 8 tens 4 hundreds	**H T O** 7 8 9	(base-ten blocks)

Order Numbers on a Number Line

Play a game with a partner. You will need a spinner. Use a paper clip and a pencil to spin.

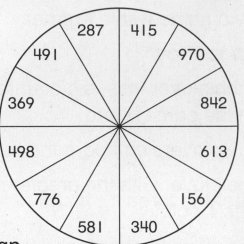

How to Play

Write your name on cards 1 and 2. Write your partner's name on 3 and 4.

• Spin a number.

• Write the number on your card if you can.

The player who fills both cards first wins.

Card 1	**Card 2**
Name _____	Name _____
Write the number that is	Write the number that is
just before _____ 416	just before _____ 157
just after 612 _____	just after 580 _____
between 286 _____ 288	between 969 _____ 971
Card 3	**Card 4**
Name _____	Name _____
Write the number that is	Write the number that is
just before _____ 777	just before _____ 370
just after 339 _____	just after 490 _____
between 841 _____ 843	between 497 _____ 499

Use with Grade 2, Chapter 22, Lesson 2, pages 417–418.

Order Numbers

Play this game with two friends. You will need three coins or counters.

How to Play

• All three players drop coins or counters on the number board below.

• Order the three numbers from least to greatest.

• The player whose number is in between the others gets one point.

The first player to get 5 points wins.

304	248	692	814	256
615	235	644	822	900
504	622	487	726	317
479	203	629	791	222
782	845	299	345	507

Name _____

Number Patterns • Algebra

Complete the patterns.
Write the numbers.

1. Start with 433	
Count by tens	_____, _____, _____, _____, _____, _____, _____

2. Start with 668	
Count by twos	_____, _____, _____, _____, _____, _____, _____

3. Start with 523	
Count by fives	_____, _____, _____, _____, _____, _____, _____

4. Start with 129	
Count by threes	_____, _____, _____, _____, _____, _____, _____

5. Start with 840	
Count by tens	_____, _____, _____, _____, _____, _____, _____

Use with Grade 2, Chapter 22, Lesson 4, pages 421–422.

Count Forward, Count Backward

Count forward or backward.
Write each number in the box.

Then count forward or backward from the new
number you wrote.

1. Start with:	Count back 100.	Count on 10.	Count back 1.
417			

2. Start with:	Count on 200.	Count back 20.	Count on 2.
573			

3. Start with:	Count back 300.	Count on 30.	Count back 3.
945			

4. Start with:	Count on 200.	Count back 30.	Count on 1.
294			

5. Start with:	Count back 100.	Count on 20.	Count back 3.
658			

6. Start with:	Count on 300.	Count back 30.	Count on 2.
360			

Add Hundreds

Play with a partner. Take turns.
Cut out the spinner.
Use a pencil and a paper clip to spin.

How to Play

• Spin a number.

• Write the number in the game card.

• Add.

The first player to reach 1,000 wins.
You lose the game if your sum is more than 1,000.

Spinner: 900, 800, 100, 700, 200, 600, 300, 500, 400

Game 1		Game 2	
Player 1	Player 2	Player 1	Player 2
☐	☐	☐	☐
+ ☐	+ ☐	+ ☐	+ ☐
☐	☐	☐	☐
+ ☐	+ ☐	+ ☐	+ ☐
☐	☐	☐	☐

Use with Grade 2, Chapter 23, Lesson 1, pages 433–434.

Regroup Ones

Choose a partner to play this addition game.
Take turns with your partner.

How to Play

• Toss two coins or counters onto the game board.

• Write the two numbers the coins hit as an addition
  problem. Solve it.

• Check your answer. If it's correct, you get one point.
  If it's wrong, you lose a turn.

The first player to get 5 points is the winner.

516	182	435	572
638	971	123	424
723	227	564	629
331	817	495	682

Regroup Tens

Choose a partner to play this regrouping game.

How to Play

• Each player chooses one set of the numbers below. Then each writes a 3-digit number. For problem 1, you might write 519, or 159, or 195, or another combination.

• Compare numbers. The player with the greater number adds the two sets of numbers.

• Each correct answer gets 2 points.

• Take 1 more point if regrouping was necessary.

The first player to get 10 points wins.

1.

_____

2.

_____

3.

_____

4.

_____

5.

_____

6.

_____

Use with Grade 2, Chapter 23, Lesson 3, pages 439–440.

Problem Solving Skill: Reading for Math
Make Inferences

Read the story.

Actors at the Theater Festival performed more than 50 short plays in less than a week. On Friday, the festival's first day, the box office sold 350 tickets. All weekend, there were special events for children. 285 children  and 400 parents came to see the jugglers and the puppet show. On Monday there were no shows and the box office was closed. On Tuesday the box office sold 722 tickets. On Wednesday it sold 793 tickets. The festival was a big hit!

1. Why do you think the box office sold so many tickets on Tuesday? _____

   _____

2. Why do you think there were no shows on Monday?

   _____

3. How many tickets were sold on Friday and Wednesday?

   _____

4. How many people saw the children's shows over the weekend?

   _____

5. Write two addition problems of your own about the story. Trade questions with a partner and write the answers.

   _____

   _____

Subtract Hundreds

Subtract. Then find your answer in the box at the bottom.
Write the letter in the box under your answer.

1.
$$900 - 500$$ $$800 - 200$$ $$700 - 500$$

☐ ☐ ☐

2.
$$300 - 200$$ $$900 - 100$$ $$800 - 100$$

☐ ☐ ☐

3.
$$800 - 300$$ $$700 - 100$$ $$900 - 300$$ $$600 - 300$$

☐ ☐ ☐ ☐ !

Read the secret message.

A = 100	G = 500	U = 200	D = 300
O = 600	Y = 400	E = 700	R = 800

Use with Grade 2, Chapter 24, Lesson 1, pages 449–450.

Name _____

Regroup Tens as Ones

The table shows how many flowers Miss Winchell sold each month.

	Roses	Daisies	Tulips	Daffodils
June	287	376	539	645
July	419	294	288	337
August	532	421	99	582

1. How many more roses were sold in July than in June?

_____ − _____ = _____

2. How many more tulips were sold in July than in August?

_____ − _____ = _____

3. How many more daisies were sold in August than in June?

_____ − _____ = _____

4. How many more daffodils were sold in June than in July?

_____ − _____ = _____

5. Write your own subtraction problem. Use the numbers in the table. Solve it. Then give it to a friend to solve. Compare answers.

_____

_____

Name _____

Regroup Hundreds as Tens

Laura and Mary play a button game.
They count all the buttons in the boxes. Then they
subtract to find the differences.
Circle the correct answers.

Buttons

Red	Blue	Green	Yellow	Purple	Orange
735	873	182	549	317	284

1. How many more red buttons
than purple buttons?

Laura 418   Mary 412

_____ – _____ = _____

2. How many more blue buttons
than green buttons?

Laura 711   Mary 691

_____ – _____ = _____

3. How many more yellow buttons
than orange buttons?

Laura 265   Mary 365

_____ – _____ = _____

4. How many more red buttons
than yellow buttons?

Laura 186   Mary 214

_____ – _____ = _____

5. How many more blue buttons
than orange buttons?

Laura 611   Mary 589

_____ – _____ = _____

Use with Grade 2, Chapter 24, Lesson 3, pages 455–456.

Name_____

Estimate, Add, and Subtract Money Amounts E 24-4 ENRICH

 yogurt
$1.49

granola bar
$1.36

 health shake
$2.80

 pita pocket
$4.16

 salad
$3.59

carob bar
$2.09

Use the prices above to add or subtract.

1. Millie buys a carob bar and a salad. How much does she spend?

_____

Jessie buys a granola bar. She pays with a $5.00 bill. How much is her change?

_____

2. Marky buys a health shake and a yogurt. About how much does he spend?

_____

Justin buys a salad. He pays with four $1.00 bills. What is his change?

_____

3. Robin buys a pita pocket, a yogurt, and a carob bar. About how much does she spend?

_____

Phyllis buys 2 yogurts and a granola bar. She pays with a $10 bill. What is her change?

_____

Buy any two items.

4. I bought a _____ and a _____. I spent

_____. I paid with a $_____ bill. My change is _____.

Unit Fractions

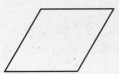

E 25-1
ENRICH

Use the 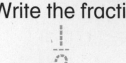 to cover each shape.

1. Draw a line to show halves.
Color one half.
Write the fraction.

$\frac{1}{2}$

_____

2. Draw lines to show fourths.
Color one fourth.
Write the fraction.

_____

3. Draw lines to show eighths.
Color one eighth.
Write the fraction.

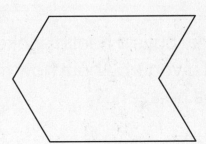

_____

What fraction of each block is shaded?

4.

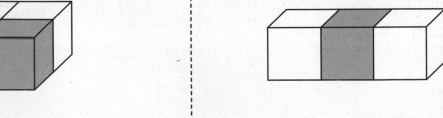

_____   _____

Use with Grade 2, Chapter 25, Lesson 1, pages 473–474.

Name _____

Fractions Equal to 1

Use pattern blocks to make shapes.

Draw the shapes. Then write the fraction for the whole.

1. Use 2 ⬯ to make a hexagon.

Color the hexagon blue.

_____

2. Use 6 △ to make a hexagon.

Color the hexagon red.

_____

3. Use 12 ☐ to make a rectangle.

Color the rectangle green.

_____

4. Use 8 ▱ to make a parallelogram.

Color the parallelogram orange.

_____

Other Fractions

Color each fraction.

1. Color $\frac{1}{4}$ blue.

Color $\frac{2}{4}$ red.

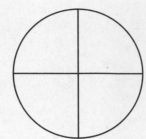

What part of the circle is colored?

_____

2. Color $\frac{1}{6}$ blue.

Color $\frac{4}{6}$ red.

What part of the circle is colored?

_____

3. Color $\frac{3}{8}$ blue.

Color $\frac{2}{8}$ red.

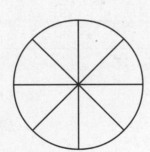

What part of the circle is colored?

_____

4. Color $\frac{1}{3}$ blue.

Color $\frac{2}{3}$ red.

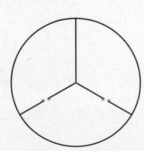

What part of the circle is colored?

_____

5. How can you tell by looking at a fraction that it equals 1?

_____

_____

Unit Fractions of a Group

1. How many horses are not gray?

_____

What fraction of the horses are not gray?

_____

_____

2. How many puppies do not have spots?

_____

What fraction of the puppies are not spotted?

_____

_____

3. How many pigs are not in the pigpen?

_____

What fraction of the pigs are not in the pigpen?

_____

Name _____

Other Fractions of a Group

The graph shows the party supplies that Betsy bought.

	Betsy's Party Supplies
party hats	🎉🎉🎉🎉🎉🎉🎉🎉
noisemakers	📯📯📯📯📯📯📯📯📯📯📯📯
balloons	🎈🎈🎈🎈🎈🎈

Color the pictures to help you solve each problem.

1. There are 8 yellow noisemakers. What fraction of the noisemakers are yellow?

_____

2. There are 3 red balloons. What fraction of the balloons are red?

_____

3. There are 6 green party hats. What fraction of the party hats are green?

_____

4. Betsy buys 4 more green hats. What fraction of the hats are green now?

_____

5. There are 15 balloons. Color 10 balloons red. What fraction of the balloons are red?

_____

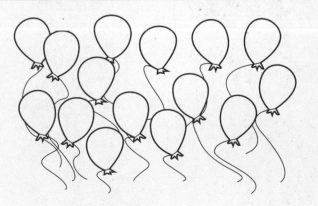

Use with Grade 2, Chapter 25, Lesson 5, pages 481–482.

Compare Fractions

Play this game with a partner. Cut out each square.

How to Play

- Put the squares face down. Each player turns over 1 card.
- The player with the greater fraction scores a point.
- Play until all the cards are turned over.

The player with more points wins.

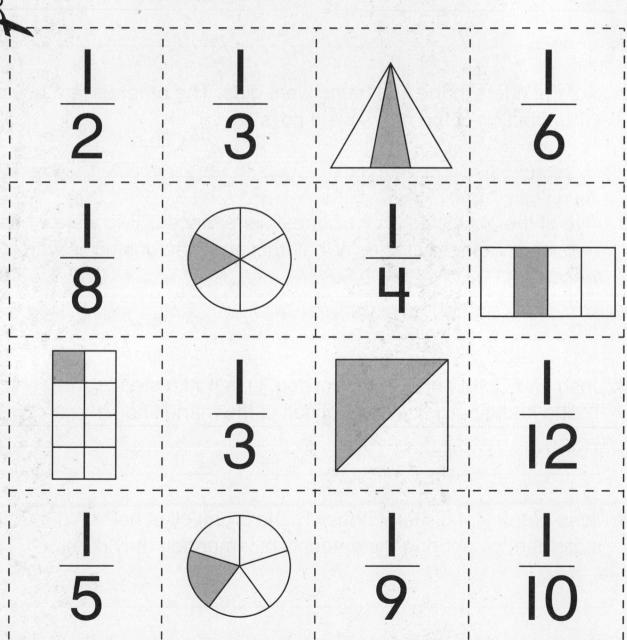

Problem Solving Skill: Reading for Math
Draw Conclusions

Josh and Luis took Carol and Tasha to a horse show.
They sat in the stands and watched the show.

Solve.

1. 2 of the horses were white. The other 12 were dark brown or black. What fraction of the horses were white?

_____

2. 6 of the riders in the first round were girls. The other 8 were boys. What fraction of the riders were boys?

_____

3. Five of the obstacles on the course were fences. Two were walls. Two were water obstacles. What fraction of the obstacles were fences?

_____

4. Josh and Carol each had a hot dog. Luis had a steak sandwich. Tasha had a burger. What fraction of the friends had burgers?

_____

5. Josh drank $\frac{1}{2}$ of his lemonade. Tasha drank all of hers. Write a statement comparing the amounts of lemonade they drank.

_____

Explore Probability

Mi Won is serving fruit at her party. Here is the fruit she will put into the bowl.

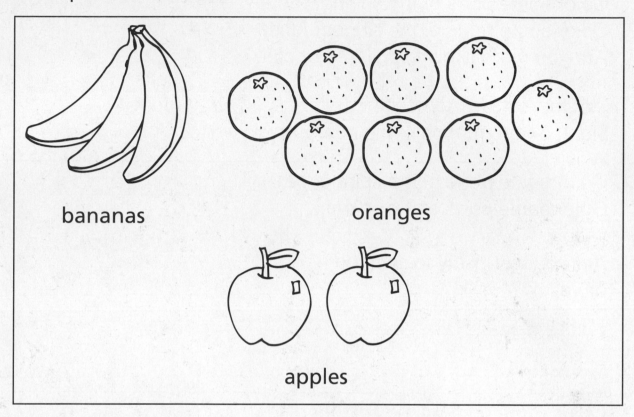

bananas

oranges

apples

Solve.

1. There are 8 oranges in the bowl. Picking an orange from the bowl without looking is _____.

   certain   probable   impossible

2. Tony picked up the bunch of bananas. The chance that he will pull a banana from the bunch is _____.

   certain   probable   impossible

3. Kamenka looks in the bowl for a grape. Taking a grape from the bowl is _____.

   certain   probable   impossible

4. There was only one piece of fruit left in the bowl after the party. The chance of it being a peach is _____.

   certain   probable   impossible

More Likely, Equally Likely, or Less Likely

You will need  red 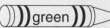 blue 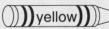 green 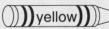 yellow 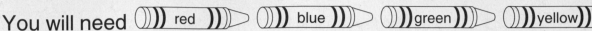 .

1. Color some parts of the spinner red.
Color some parts of the spinner blue.
Are you more likely to spin red or blue?

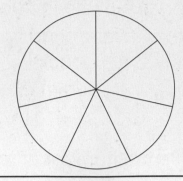

_____

2. Color some parts of the spinner red.
Color some parts of the spinner yellow.
Are you less likely to spin red or yellow?

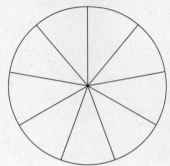

_____

3. Color some parts of the spinner blue.
Color some parts of the spinner yellow.
Color some parts of the spinner green.
Are you most likely to spin blue, green, or yellow?

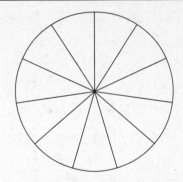

_____

4. How could you color the spinner in problem 2 to make it equally likely to spin any of the colors?

_____

_____

Make Predictions

Put 5 red cubes and 5 blue cubes in a bag.
Pick one cube without looking.
Mark the tally chart for the color you picked.
Put the cube back in the bag.
Pick cubes and mark the tally chart 10 times in all.

red	blue

Write the number of red cubes and blue cubes you picked.

1. I picked _____ red cubes.

2. I picked _____ blue cubes.

What if you try this again?

How many of each color will you pick this time?

3. I will pick _____ red cubes.

4. I will pick _____ blue cubes.

Now try it again.

Pick cubes and mark the tally chart.

Do it 10 times in all.

See if your prediction was correct.

red	blue

Range and Mode

The zoo has special movies about jungle animals.

The pictograph shows how many tickets were sold for each show.

Movie Ticket Sales

Big Cats	🎟🎟🎟🎟
Leaping Lizards	🎟🎟🎟🎟🎟
Jungle Birds	🎟🎟🎟🎟🎟🎟🎟
Monkey Business	🎟🎟🎟🎟🎟🎟🎟🎟
Baby Elephants	🎟🎟🎟🎟

Each 🎟 stands for 2 tickets.

Read the graph. How many tickets were sold for each show?

Big Cats	Leaping Lizards	Jungle Birds	Monkey Business	Baby Elephants

1. What is the range of the data? _____ tickets

2. What is the mode of the data? _____ tickets

3. What was the total number of tickets sold? _____ tickets

Use with Grade 2, Chapter 27, Lesson 1, pages 509–510.

Median

Play a game. Take turns with a partner.

How to Play

• Drop a coin or counter on the target 5 times.

• Write down the numbers you hit.

• Find the median.

• If the median is 9 or less, you get 2 points.
  If it is 10 or greater, you get 1 point.

The first player to reach 10 points wins.

4	16	3	13
2	12	8	6
11	1	7	14
9	15	5	10

Coordinate Graphs • Algebra

Write directions to find each place on the map.

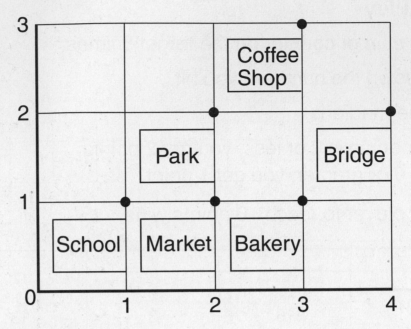

1. Where is the bakery?

Right _____ Up _____

_____

2. Where is the market?

Right _____ Up _____

_____

3. Where is the park?

Right _____ Up _____

_____

4. Where is the coffee shop?

Right _____ Up _____

   Use with Grade 2, Chapter 27, Lesson 3, pages 513–514.

Line Graphs

Use the data below to graph the weather over the week of February 9–15. Then answer the questions.

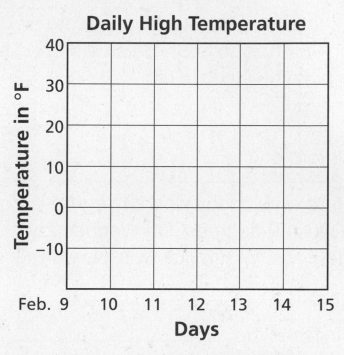

Daily High Temperature

It got very cold in the middle of February. On February 9, the temperature was 35 degrees. On February 10 and 11, the temperature held steady at 20 degrees. On February 12, it fell to 15 degrees. On February 13, it dropped to 0. On February 14, the temperature was −5 degrees. February 15 was a little warmer, at 5 degrees above zero.

1. On which two days was the temperature the same?

_____

2. Which day was the coldest?

_____

3. Which day was the warmest?

_____

4. On which day was the temperature 15 degrees?

_____

Problem Solving Skill: Reading for Math

Important and Unimportant Information

Solve each problem. Identify the unimportant information.

1. Greg studied math for one hour. Then he ate an apple. He studied science for half an hour. He studied Spanish for one hour. How long did he study in all?

   _____ hours

   Unimportant information: _____

2. The temperature on Monday was 20 degrees. It snowed on Tuesday and was 30 degrees. On Wednesday it snowed again and was 32 degrees. Which day was the warmest?

   _____

   Unimportant information: _____

3. Jamaica goes to ballet class on Fridays. On Saturdays she has a music lesson. She has played piano for 3 years. On Sundays Jamaica goes to gymnastics practice. How many activities does Jamaica have each week?

   _____ activities

   Unimportant information: _____

4. There are 44 posters on the restaurant's walls. 9 are written in English. 12 are in French. The rest are in Italian. 7 posters show ads for circuses or plays. 5 are travel posters. How many more posters are written in Italian than French?

   _____ more posters written in Italian

   Unimportant information: _____

Use with Grade 2, Chapter 27, Lesson 5, pages 517–518.

Explore Equal Groups

Write how many groups.
Write how many in each group.
Write how many in all.

1.

_____ groups of _____ = _____

2.

_____ groups of _____ = _____

3.

_____ groups of _____ = _____

---

4. OO OO OO OO

_____ groups of _____ = _____

5. OOO OOO OOO OOO
OO   OO   OO   OO

_____ groups of _____ = _____

---

6. OOOOO OOOOO
OOOOO OOOOO

_____ groups of _____ = _____

7. OO OO OO OO OO

_____ groups of _____ = _____

Repeated Addition and Multiplication

E 28-2
ENRICH

Draw the groups.
Write an addition and a multiplication sentence.

1. Draw 3 groups of 2.

____ + ____ + ____ = ____

____ × ____ = ____

2. Draw 2 groups of 4.

____ + ____ = ____

____ × ____ = ____

3. Draw 3 groups of 3.

____ + ____ + ____ = ____

____ × ____ = ____

4. Draw 3 groups of 1.

____ + ____ + ____ = ____

____ × ____ = ____

5. Draw 5 groups of 3.

____ + ____ + ____ + ____ + ____ = ____

____ × ____ = ____

Use with Grade 2, Chapter 28, Lesson 2, pages 527–528.

Use Arrays to Multiply

28-3
ENRICH

Look at each pattern. Draw the next array.
Write the multiplication sentence.

1. [array]

___ × ___ = ___

2. [array]

___ × ___ = ___

3.

___ × ___ = ___

---

4. [array]

___ × ___ = ___

5. [array]

___ × ___ = ___

6.

___ × ___ = ___

---

7. [array]

___ × ___ = ___

8. [array]

___ × ___ = ___

9.

___ × ___ = ___

10. Look at the products in problem 1.
What counting pattern do you see?

Count by _____.

Repeated Subtraction and Division

Subtract. Find the rule.

Then name the counting pattern.

1.

Rule: Subtract _____	
In	Out
10	8
8	6
6	
4	
2	

Pattern: Count back by _____.

2.

Rule: Subtract _____	
In	Out
15	12
12	
9	6
6	
3	0

Pattern: Count back by _____.

3.

Rule: Subtract _____	
In	Out
20	16
16	
	8
8	
4	0

Pattern: Count back by _____.

4.

Rule: Subtract _____	
In	Out
25	20
20	15
15	
	5
5	

Pattern: Count back by _____.

Use with Grade 2, Chapter 28, Lesson 4, pages 533–534.

Divide to Find Equal Shares

Find each quotient. Then solve the puzzle.

1. $8 \div 2 =$ ____ **S**	**2.** $12 \div 3 =$ ____ **S**	**3.** $3\overline{)21}$ **T**
4. $18 \div 3 =$ ____ **H**	**5.** $5 \div 5 =$ ____ **C**	**6.** $2\overline{)4}$ **A**
7. $10 \div 2 =$ ____ **U**	**8.** $16 \div 2 =$ ____ **E**	**9.** $3\overline{)9}$ **M**
10. $6 \div 3 =$ ____ **A**	**11.** $16 \div 4 =$ ____ **S**	**12.** $2\overline{)14}$ **T**
13. $20 \div 5 =$ ____ **S**		

Write the letter that goes with each quotient. The letters will tell you the name of the state where the Pilgrims landed at Plymouth Rock.

3	2	4	4	2	1	6	5	4	8	7	7	4